ACTIVITY SUPERCHARGES YOUR LIFE

···

C·R·E·A·T·I·O·N Health

LIFE GUIDE #4

For Individual Study and Small Group Use

CREATION Health Life Guide #4
Copyright © MMXIII by Florida Hospital
Published by Florida Hospital Publishing
900 Winderley Place, Suite 1600
Maitland, Florida 32751

To Extend *the* Health *and* Healing Ministry *of* Christ

Publisher and Editor-in-Chief:	Todd Chobotar
Managing Editor:	David Biebel, DMin
Production:	Lillian Boyd
Promotion:	Laurel Prizigley
Copy Editor:	Pamela Nordberg
Author Photography:	Timothy Brown
Design:	Carter Design, Inc., Denver, CO
Peer Reviewers:	Amaryllis Sanchez-Wohlever, MD; Robert Hayes
	Bradford Eakins, MDiv; Karen Tilstra, PhD
	Andy McDonald, DMin; Gerald Wasmer, MDiv
	Paul Campoli, MDiv; Barbara Olsen, MACL
	Rick Szilagyi, DMin; Andre VanHeerden
	Tim Goff, MDiv; Sabine Vatel, DMin

PUBLISHER'S NOTE: This book is not intended to replace a one-on-one relationship with a qualified healthcare professional, but as a sharing of knowledge and information from the research and experience of the author. You are advised and encouraged to consult with your healthcare professional in all matters relating to your health and the health of your family. The publisher and author disclaim any liability arising directly or indirectly from the use of this book.

The author assumes full responsibility for the accuracy of all facts and quotations as cited in this book. CREATION Health is a registered trademark of Florida Hospital. All rights reserved.

Unless otherwise indicated, all Scripture quotations are taken from the Holy Bible, New Living Translation, copyright © 1996, 2004 by Tyndale House Publishers, Inc., Wheaton, Illinois 60189. All other Scripture references are from the following sources: The Holy Bible, New International Version (NIV), copyright © 1973, 1978, 1984 by Biblica, Inc. Used by permission of Zondervan. The Holy Bible, Revised Standard Version (RSV), copyright © 1946, 1952, 1971 by the National Council of the Churches of Christ. The Holy Bible, King James Version (KJV). The Holy Bible, New King James Version (NKJV), copyright © 1982 by Thomas Nelson, Inc. The Message (MSG), copyright© by Eugene H. Peterson 1993, 1994, 1995, 1996, 2000, 2001, 2002. Used by permission of NAVPress Publishing Group. All Scriptures used by permission. All rights reserved.

For volume discounts please contact special sales at:
HealthProducts@FLHosp.org | 407-303-1929

Printed in the United States of America.
PR 14 13 12 11 10 9 8 7 6 5 4 3 2 1
ISBN: 978-0-9887406-3-1

For more life-changing resources visit:
FloridaHospitalPublishing.com
Healthy100Churches.org
CREATIONHealth.com
Healthy100.org

CONTENTS

DOWNLOAD YOUR FREE LEADER RESOURCE

Are you a small group leader? We've created a special resource to help you lead an effective CREATION Health discussion group. Download at: **CREATION**Health.com/LeaderResources

WELCOME TO CREATION HEALTH

Congratulations on your choice to use this resource to improve your life! Whether you are new to the concept of CREATION Health or are a seasoned expert, this book was created for you. CREATION Health is a faith-based health and wellness program based on the Bible's Creation story. This book is part of a Life Guide series seeking to help you apply eight elegantly simple principles for living life to the full.

The letters of the CREATION acronym stand for:

C CHOICE

R REST

E ENVIRONMENT

A ACTIVITY

T TRUST

I INTERPERSONAL

O OUTLOOK

N NUTRITION

In John 10:10 Jesus said, "I have come that they may have life, and have it to the full" (NIV). The Greek word used for life is "zoe," which means the absolute fullness of life…genuine life…a life that is active, satisfying, and filled with joy.

That is why CREATION Health takes a life-transforming approach to total person wellness – mentally, physically, spiritually, and socially – with the eight universal principles of health. Where did these principles come from?

The book of Genesis describes how God created the earth and made a special garden called Eden as a home for his first two children, Adam and Eve. One of the first and finest gifts given to them was abundant health. By examining the Creation story we can learn much about feeling fit and living long, fulfilling lives today.

As you begin this journey toward an improved lifestyle, remember that full health is more than the absence of disease and its symptoms. It's a realization that God desires each of his children – people like you and me whom he loves and cares about – to have the best that this life can offer. It is trusting that your Creator has a plan for your life.

Is there any good parent who doesn't want the best for their child? No. So it makes sense that God would want his best for us. Naturally, human freedom of choice sometimes makes life messy, so not everything can or will be perfect as it once was. But that doesn't mean we shouldn't take a good look at the earliest records of humans found in the Bible to see if there is something special that can be gleaned.

This book – and the other seven in the Life Guide series – takes a deep dive into CREATION Health and translates the fundamental concepts into easy-to-follow steps. These guides include many questions designed to help you or your small group plumb the depths of every principle and learn strategies for integrating the things you learn into everyday life. As a result, you will discover that embracing the CREATION Health prescription can help restore health, happiness, balance, and joy to life.

The CREATION Health Lifestyle has a long, proven history of wellness and longevity – worldwide! People just like you are making a few simple changes in their lives and living longer, fuller lives. They are getting healthy, staying healthy, and are able to do the things they love, well into their later years. Now is the time to join them by transforming your habits into a healthy lifestyle.

If you would like to learn more about the many resources available, visit **CREATIONHealth.com**. If you would like to learn more about how to live to a Healthy 100, visit **Healthy100.org** or visit **Healthy100Churches.org**.

Welcome to CREATION Health,

Todd Chobotar
Publisher and Editor-in-Chief

BRAIN FITNESS

LESSON ONE

WARM UP

PART A – Choose one or both questions to discuss.[1]

1. Which room in your home do you enjoy the most? Why?

2. If you could be in charge of the world for one day, what specific thing would you do, and for which group of people?

Part B – Activity Time.

The overall theme of these lessons is the importance of becoming more active. If you are studying this lesson in a group, the following is a mental activity that group members can do together.

Identify each phrase using the clues provided.[2] Work in teams of two for two minutes, then everyone compares answers. (Compare answers only at the end of the lesson after the entire group has finished trying.)

    a.   **GENE   RATION**

    b.   **tHE HAND**

    c.   **NOOS**

    d.   **X☐**

    e.   **RAKED**

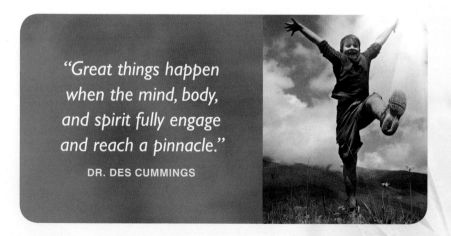

"Great things happen when the mind, body, and spirit fully engage and reach a pinnacle."

DR. DES CUMMINGS

DISCOVERY

My mind hit some potholes recently. Nothing major so far, just a series of random memory lapses. A couple of examples:

First example: My wife sent me to the grocery store a few weeks ago for two items. I didn't write them down, refusing to admit to myself that I might not be able to remember just two measly items. I was also instructed to get whatever else I thought might be useful. Entering the store, I grabbed a cart and wandered around, foolishly thinking I'd get the "whatever else" products out of the way first. I chose milk, ingredients for my famous goulash, bread, cereal, pancake mix, frozen burritos, and yogurt.

That done, I started in on my wife's needs. To my everlasting credit, I did remember bananas. But as to her second request, I drew a complete blank. I tried to recall her voice, "Now be sure and get bananas and _____." Nothing. Beads of sweat stood out on my forehead. "Bananas and _____," I repeated several times mentally. At the very last moment, within five feet of the checkout, it hit me – trash bags. Kind of disconcerting.

> *My mind hit some potholes recently. Nothing major so far, just a series of random memory lapses.*

Second example: My wife and I were chatting amicably with a couple of longtime friends in our living room not long ago. The topic turned to a schoolmate from the 1970s named Bob. I listened to the conversation, then decided to chime in myself. "Yah," I said, "I remember the time

when…" The next word was supposed to be the guy's name, but it suddenly escaped me. Complete blank. My mind raced, knowing that if I didn't come up with it very quickly the too-long pause would give the impression that my mind was turning into oatmeal mush. After three agonizing seconds, I remembered and blurted out too loudly, "Bob," then hurried on to finish my sentence, somewhat rattled.

Such garden variety episodes of forgetfulness need not be cause for concern, but as we get older they tend to underscore our fear of eventually slipping into some degree of dementia. We all know that in society at large, mental decline is tragically widespread as people get more and more birthdays under their belts.

That sad story, however, can be rewritten. New research is getting a much better handle on how to keep our brains in great working order far beyond what most people used to think possible. Scientists are discovering effective ways for us to maintain brain fitness just like we can maintain the fitness of our heart, lungs, and muscles. To a large extent, we can now take back significant control over the condition of our minds and proactively play a major role in determining what kind of brain we carry into the future.[3]

The essence of how the brain works centers on connections that are made between brain cells called neurons. Every thought, emotion, or action is rooted in an electrical signal traveling along networks of thousands and thousands of neurons.

During the formative years, our brains expand dramatically. So much new information, so many new experiences. But the further we journey into adulthood, the more life gets reduced to a series of routines, doing mostly the same things in the same old way.[4] We settle into a comfort zone, giving priority to peace and restfulness. All of this is understandable, but our brains suffer as a result.

As the pace at which new networks are formed slows, we become more vulnerable to mental decline. Just as unused muscles tend to atrophy, the underused portions of our brains become less agile, less able to accommodate new challenges, or recall facts and memories. Seldom-employed mental pathways become overgrown with weeds.

An antidote to slow mental regression is to proactively build new networks and activate millions of dormant neurons – the earlier the better. The greater the number of pathways we form on an ongoing basis, the less vulnerable we are to the mental inroads of aging. Such networks form a bulwark against intellectual sluggishness and decay.[5]

But what is the best way to form those new pathways? What methods are most effective?

Enter the science of "Neurobics." The word was coined by Lawrence C. Katz, James Duke Professor of Neurobiology at Duke University Medical Center. It is an intentional takeoff on "aerobics," the familiar word for physical exercise. Neurobics is all about *mental* exercises and fitness. It encompasses the revolutionary new physiological understanding of how to grow our brains and maximize their effectiveness.[6] If it were a pill, it would be in every medicine cabinet in the country.

Our brains love new adventures
and new ways of doing things.
Novelty is a big hit with neurons.
They can't get enough of it.

Neurobics provides us with several guidelines that can turbo-charge our mental processes and transform our brains. These guidelines won't turn us into geniuses or give us photographic memories, but they will make our minds much healthier and effective by engaging more and more of our neural networks in stimulating, impactful ways. The following list covers several key strategies:

1. Enter into novel experiences.

Our brains love new adventures and new ways of doing things. Novelty is a big hit with neurons. They can't get enough of it. They react like kids on Christmas morning. Ericka P. Simpson, MD, from the Methodist Hospital System Neurological Institute in Houston, comments, "When you challenge the brain with new skills and new ways of doing things, it increases connections in the brain [and] synaptic density."[7]

To qualify as truly novel, something has to be nontrivial, a clear break with the past. It needs to be unusual, surprising, and, whenever possible, fun.[8]

For instance, writing with a pencil rather than a pen is too small a change to score very high on the novelty scale. Instead, take whatever writing implement you choose *and use the other hand*.[9] Or use the computer mouse with the other hand.[10] That really gets the brain's attention.

If you are right handed, the difficult skill of writing that you mastered years ago is handled by the left side of the brain. It is a complex task that involves a large network of connections and circuitry. When you change hands, all that practice, all that well-honed ability, is suddenly out the window because you are switching the side of your brain that gets activated. The newly employed hemisphere comes to full attention and says, "Hey, what's going on here? How come I have to do this?" It is an experience your brain is not likely to soon forget. And lo and behold, you've built whole new pathways using a new set of underemployed neurons. You don't have to switch permanently to have the desired effect, just periodically for a few minutes at a time.

Other examples of novel behavior are:

- Leave for work fifteen minutes early and take a new route.

- Listen to a different radio station with different music.

- Go out to eat as a family or with friends and agree to communicate only nonverbally using hand gestures, expressions, and body language (speak to the servers verbally, however).[11]

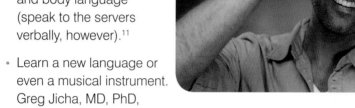

- Learn a new language or even a musical instrument. Greg Jicha, MD, PhD, assistant professor of neurology at the University of Kentucky College of Medicine, tells the story of an eighty-two-year-old who learned to play the trumpet. Jicha continues, "I've heard people say, 'You can't teach an old dog new tricks.' That can't be further from the truth."[12]

The list of possibilities is endless. Enter into new adventures. Choose to step outside your comfort zone on a regular basis – for your brain's sake.

2. Utilize all of your senses.

The human brain interacts with the world around it through our five senses – vision, hearing, smell, taste, and touch. The inputs from these senses do not all go to the same place in our brain. Many different areas are impacted and employed. And these various regions also interact to make tons of associations.

For example, you smell a certain kind of rose and your mind travels back to your first wedding anniversary when your hubby gave you a dozen red roses, which brings to mind the rundown apartment you lived in at the time and the early morning train that sounded its horn at two a.m.[13] Because of these multiple associations and interactions, utilization of our senses has a long lasting, broad-based effect on our billions of neurons.[14]

As adults, our strong tendency is to rely almost exclusively on vision and hearing because they are the quickest ways to glean information from our surroundings. The marvelous senses of touch, taste, and smell tend to fade into the background, and our brains long for them to be reactivated in a robust way.

Try, for example, to navigate around your house with your eyes closed (be careful!). All of a sudden the sense of vision we rely on almost exclusively is unavailable and our other senses go on full alert. "Which side of the door was that light switch on?" "What is that smell?" "Is that the sound of the refrigerator turning on?"[15]

Try new smells. Put a bottle of vanilla extract on your nightstand and take a whiff of it every morning for the next couple weeks. Then switch it out for another.[16] Touch new textures. Taste new foods. Listen to nature. Look more closely at the details of your world.

The human brain interacts with the world around it through our five senses – vision, hearing, smell, taste, and touch.

3. Engage your emotions.

The brain circuits for emotions are just as tangible as those for our senses. Scans have now confirmed the powerful influence emotions have on creating memories. The more emotionally loaded a situation is, the more the memory will persist.[17] Doing activities with others should be a vital part of your Neurobics strategy because human interactions are so often fraught with a mix of feelings from laughter to empathy. Social connections stimulate the brain in a variety of positive ways. As we age, our social circle tends to shrink, so in order to keep mentally fit, we need to proactively seek out ways to interface with the world and people around us.

4. Try your hand at games and puzzles.

According to Tom Perls, MD, MPH, associate professor of medicine at Boston University Medical Center and head of the New England Centenarian Study, games that grow your brain should focus on such concepts as recall and retention, problem-solving and strategy, word building, tracking, perception, spatial skills, and body movement.[18] Such activities can help delay potential memory loss and mental decline.

5. Bible study.

In the New Testament book of Hebrews, we read,

> *"For the word of God is living, and active, and sharper than any two-edged sword, and piercing even to the dividing of soul and spirit, of both joints and marrow, and quick to discern the thoughts and intents of the heart" (Hebrews 4:12, ASV).*

The Scriptures capture the essence of life like no other work of literature. With its biographies, adventures, wisdom, insights, vision, and focus on the eternal, no other book is so well calculated to expand the mind and imagination as the Bible. It will stir the creation of countless new pathways in the brain as its words challenge us to higher thinking and deeper living.

In light of what we now know about the importance of brain fitness, the words of the apostle Paul take on new meaning, "Do not conform to the pattern of this world, but be transformed by the *renewing of your mind.* Then you will be able to test and approve what God's will is – his good, pleasing and perfect will" (Romans 12:2, NIV, emphasis added).

Jesus practiced "brain fitness" by mastering the art of teaching in parables. It is very hard to create mini-stories that are as succinct, captivating, and relevant as his were. Try it sometime! He also tried to create brain fitness in others by ending his parables with a question to get them thinking deeply about spiritual truth.

Answers to "Action Time" (Page 7)

- a. Generation Gap
- b. A bird in the hand
- c. Back soon
- d. Times Square
- e. Half baked

> *Jesus practiced "brain fitness" by mastering the art of teaching in parables.*

DISCUSSION

Describe a time when you experienced a recent incident of garden variety forgetfulness.

....

....

How would you define "Neurobics"? What benefit might it have as you consider being more mentally active?

....

....

Share a new fact you learned recently outside of this lesson.

....

....

Describe a novel experience you have had recently.

....

....

Describe a special memory that is linked to a certain scent or smell.

....

....

What puzzles do you enjoy doing? Why?

....

....

What Bible verse or story would you characterize as being especially stimulating mentally?

....

....

Think of two activities you could do in the next few weeks to apply this lesson.

....

....

SHARING

OPPORTUNITY #1

If you are studying this book with a group, this section is about an opportunity for you to be a blessing to someone outside of your small group and also to deepen the impact of the lesson on your own life. The group is encouraged to discuss at the end of each meeting what aspects of the lesson they might like to share with someone at home, work, or in the community if the opportunity arises. There is an "Abundant Living Thought" at the end of each lesson as one possibility of something to pass along.

Start each day asking God to provide opportunities to share, and then keep your radar up.

You can be an ambassador and reach people with the good news that abundant living is available to all.

ABUNDANT LIVING THOUGHT

Our brains love new adventures and new ways of doing things. Novelty is a big hit with neurons.

PHYSICAL ACTIVITY
BENEFITS THE BRAIN

LESSON TWO

WARM UP

Feedback: In what ways did God open the door last week for you to share some part of the lesson with someone else?

....

....

Part A – Choose one or both questions to discuss.[19]

1. If you were on a quiz show, what category would you feel most knowledgeable about?

2. One of the hardest things to learn in life is _____.

Part B – Activity Time.
The overall theme of these lessons is the importance of becoming more active. This lesson and the ones that follow include a physical activity for group members to do together now and to incorporate into their lifestyles afterward.

Stand up and turn your body from side to side while swinging your arms for thirty seconds. Don't hit your neighbor, if studying in a group setting.

Notice: Next week (Lesson 3) is "Show and Tell," for those studying in a group. Each person should prepare to bring something that represents an aspect of themselves, past or present, that others probably don't know about.

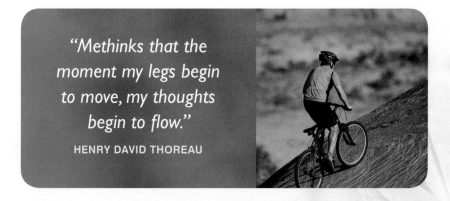

"Methinks that the moment my legs begin to move, my thoughts begin to flow."

HENRY DAVID THOREAU

DISCOVERY

In the previous lesson we learned about ways to exercise the brain itself in order to keep it fit and happy. In this lesson we'll explore how becoming physically active can help the brain as well. The more our bodies move, the more our brains will benefit. To illustrate the importance of movement for brain development from our earliest days, imagine the following diary from the perspective of an unborn infant:

DIARY OF AN UNBORN BABY

Month 8, day 20 – That thumping sound is comforting, but, to be honest, it's starting to get to me. All day and night, like a drumbeat, over and over and over. I really need a break.

Month 8, day 21 – Water, water everywhere. I live in a Jacuzzi. Fingers pruney. Wish I had a toy boat.

Month 8, day 22 – Hearing better every day. Love that country music station Mom cranks up on the way to work.[20]

Month 8, day 23 – More churning and sloshing behind me than usual. Mom probably pigged out for lunch.

Month 8, day 24 – Nature could hit the eject button anytime now. Got to review my checklist and start cleaning up in here. Don't want Doc to think I'm a slob. "Leave it like you found it," kind of thing.

Month 8, day 25 – We're tipping to the left. Getting pulled to one side. Bedtime for Mom. She can really snore!

Month 8, day 26 – If it weren't for this cord thing, I'd have nothing to play with at all. Another day of waiting. Boooorrring!

Month 8, day 27 – Scary morning! The walls kinda pushed in on me a little. Never happened before. Thought maybe this was it, but everything settled down.

Month 8, day 28 – I gotta keep up my calisthenics. Kick, punch, kick, punch, kick, kick. Left, right. It's one of the best things I can do to get my brain ready for the outside world. Gotta be sharp for the nurses' exam after my big appearance!

I'm guessing that nothing in the journal surprised you very much until you got to day 28 and the mention of the brain. Our precocious unborn got it right. All the kicking and punching that causes Mom to laugh and wince at the same time is a major key to developing the baby's brand-new brain. In-womb movement and activity are essential to building brain cells and networks among the billions of neurons.[21]

This early biological connection between physical activity and a healthy brain sets up a blueprint for what is supposed to continue for the rest of our lives. Our brains depend on regular body movement to function the way they were intended to by our Creator.

After our little, diary-keeping baby has been born, he or she will eventually begin to roll, creep, crawl. I used to think these activities were important only for developing arm and leg muscles. But these movements are actually an important part of infant brain development.[22] During the first year, the young one's brain will grow faster than at any other time, and one of the best things parents can do to enhance mental progress is to foster movement and play.[23]

As our infant enters the childhood years, the need for regular, brain-enhancing movement continues unabated. Myriad possibilities can be as simple as marching to a beat on the way to the bathroom, animal walks mimicking the child's favorite stuffed animals, rhythmic body movements to music, doing scaled-down calisthenics with the parents, and on and on.[24]

Unfortunately, children in today's society are at high risk of falling victim to the widespread trend toward inactivity. Sadly, kids are becoming much more sedentary. Instead of tying on their sneakers and heading out the door after school, they spend more and more hours surfing the Internet, competing in video games, and texting friends. Nothing less than their brain's health is at stake. Balance is key. Parents need to be role models of how to take advantage of technology while at the same time highly valuing an active lifestyle.

As children grow up and become adults, the important linkage between physical activity and brain health remains. It is also a time, however, when we, too, often settle further into sedentary living. The foundation of activity that characterized the unborn and infant is broken up and ignored. We forget that movement is just as crucial now as it was then.

An active lifestyle keeps our heart, lungs, muscles, and various organs in good working order. *But its greatest value is how it benefits the brain.*[25] All else is secondary. If our brains don't work at their best, our quality of life is compromised and we can remain at arm's length from optimal living.

In many ways, the primary purpose of our bodies is to serve the brain. We have our various senses so that our brain can interact with the outside world. We have legs to take it where it wants to go. We have arms and hands to accomplish what it wants to do. The brain is king/queen. Every time your heart beats, fully 25 percent of your blood flows up between your ears. That should tell us something about the body's priorities.

I have never met my brain personally, but I do feel the need to express more appreciation. It is obviously working very hard. No breaks. No vacations. On duty as CEO, 24/7. It sends countless electrical signals zipping along millions of networks at over two hundred miles per hour and thinks about seventy thousand thoughts a day – all on less power than it takes to run a twenty-five-watt light bulb.[26]

My brain enabled me to make the peanut butter and banana sandwich I just ate for an energy boost ten minutes ago. It moves my fingers across the computer keyboard and chooses the right keys. That seemingly simple task is enormously difficult from a neurological point of view. My brain coordinates all the phenomenally complex biological machinery from my neck down. It keeps me from writing nonsense (mostly). And yet how often have I said a simple "thank-you." Actually… never!

So here it is: THANK-YOU, MY BRAIN!

I also should apologize for not being as physically active as I ought to be. So many new mental pathways could be developed that would lead me into deeper dimensions of holistic health, and yet on too many days I sit around and say, "Tomorrow." I've settled for less than my brain needs. SORRY!

(I'll be back in a few minutes. I'm taking an activity break for my brain's sake.)

(I'm back.) There, I feel much better.

> *Parents need to be role models of how to take advantage of technology while at the same time highly valuing an active lifestyle.*

If you choose to show how much you appreciate your own brain by engaging in regular physical activity and movement, you can typically expect to enjoy the following benefits mentally:

1. Keeps your brain more youthful.

As we have seen, since the time we were in the womb, activity has helped build brain cells and connect neurons into new networks. The more networks formed, the more effective and fit our brains become.

Also, the more fit our heart and lungs are, the more effectively they can nourish the brain with oxygen and nutrients. Every minute, our brain needs the equivalent of three soda cans full of blood.[27] Exercise increases the level of the gas nitric oxide, which widens blood vessels, creating greater blood flow.[28]

2. Fosters higher brain functioning.

Activity enhances what are called the "executive functions" of the brain. These include things like planning, decision making, problem solving, memory, conflict resolution, multitasking, and the ability to focus without being distracted.[29] Excellence in these areas has a direct bearing on our quality of life.

3. Reduces the corrosive impact of stress.

When we experience significant ongoing stress, our bodies react by producing extra amounts of a hormone called cortisol. Its role is to prepare us for either "fight or flight" by triggering increased energy and higher blood pressure. If the elevated level of cortisol persists, it can damage the region of the brain called the hippocampus and interfere with vital neurotransmitters that enable brain cells to communicate with one another.[30]

One of the best antidotes is physical exertion of some type. Even a little bit can go a long way. Physical activity boosts the production of endorphins, the feel-good neurotransmitters in the brain that calm us and keep the stress response in check.[31] It also enhances the production of serotonin to stave off depression, and dopamine to increase motivation.[32]

4. Sets the stage for greater learning.

Remarkably, the same part of the brain processes both learning and movement. In fact, movement and learning are in constant interaction with each other.[33] Taking advantage of this new understanding, an increasing number of schools are carving out more time for activity during the school day. Because of the clear linkage between activity and learning, guidance counselors in one school often help students arrange their schedules to include some type of exercise class prior to their hardest subjects.[34]

The Centers for Disease Control (CDC) reports on a 2003 analysis called the National Youth Risk Behavior Study (YRBS) that demonstrates the negative impact inactivity has on learning.[35] To counter the results of the YRBS study, the CDC has proactively made recommendations for schools to integrate more movement into regular classroom time itself. Mayo Clinic researcher James Levine, MD, PhD asks us to imagine a school where "children are moving *as part of their lessons.*"[36]

The vital connection between movement and learning is not limited to young people but continues throughout our lifetime. An active lifestyle enables the brain to better assimilate new information and expand its learning in the classroom of life.[37]

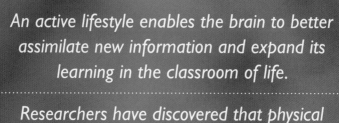

An active lifestyle enables the brain to better assimilate new information and expand its learning in the classroom of life.

Researchers have discovered that physical activity can significantly reduce the risk of mental impairment and dementia in older adults.

5. Protects you against mental impairment and dementia.

Researchers have discovered that physical activity can significantly reduce the risk of mental impairment and dementia in older adults. One study in particular involved 3,075 adults, ages seventy to seventy-nine. In a review of previous research, they discovered that the focus had been only on the benefits of traditional workouts.

Instead, these researchers chose to focus on what they called "Activity Energy Expenditure" (AEE), which encompasses total movement throughout the day of varying intensities, including non-exercise activities such as housework, shopping, going up and down stairs, and how often someone stood up from sitting. This approach produced a much more solid basis for the conclusion that an active lifestyle offers significant protection against mental decline.[38] Wendy Bumgardner writes, "They found the more active a person is, the less brain decline they experienced."[39]

Considering the significance of the five points on the above list, it is clear that brain-benefiting physical activity needs to be integrated in a comprehensive way into our overall lifestyles. Whatever gets our heart pumping faster and our muscles working harder will most certainly cause our brains to smile. Think of physical movement as a gift you can give to your hard-working, faithful, loyal, amazing brain so it can fulfill its dreams for your future.

When God created Adam and Eve, he placed them in a lush garden home filled with an incredible variety of trees, bushes, plants, and flowers. Knowing the vital connection between physical activity and excellent mental health, God told the newlyweds to "work it and take care of it" (Gen. 2:15, NIV). Another translation says they were to "cultivate it" (MSG). The young couple were the world's first gardeners and landscapers. I know how much effort it takes to maintain my little yard, so they were no doubt busy in this happy, fulfilling endeavor.

So it is for us today. One of the best ways to cooperate with God is to keep our minds fit through regular physical movement and activity. We honor him when we care for and develop the marvelous brain he has so graciously provided.

DISCUSSION

What other thoughts and impressions might you include in the unborn baby's imaginary diary?

....

....

Which of the "executive functions" of the brain would you be most interested in improving through greater physical movement? Why?

....

....

Describe how physical activity has helped to reduce your stress level.

....

....

Discuss what a classroom that fostered more movement during regular class time might look like.

....

....

What is the difference between focusing on "workouts" and on total "activity energy expenditure"? Why is that important?

....

....

If you are a parent, how can you make activity an important part of your child's homework each night?

....

....

Please finish the sentence, "Thank-you, brain, for…"

....

....

If your brain could write a letter to you to help motivate you to become more active, what might it say? How would that help?

....

....

SHARING

OPPORTUNITY #2

- Pray for God to open the way for you to share something from these lessons to help someone else this week.

- Keep your radar up each day for opportunities.

ABUNDANT LIVING THOUGHT

Think of physical movement as a gift you can give to your brain so it can fulfill its dreams for your future.

YOU CAN'T
SIT THERE

LESSON THREE

WARM UP

Feedback: In what ways did God open the door last week for you to share some part of the lessons with someone else?

....

....

....

....

Part A – In a group setting, this week is "Show and Tell."

Each person brings something that represents an aspect of themselves, past or present, that others probably don't know about. Each person has up to one minute to tell their story.

Part B – Activity Time.

Everyone stand up and march in place for thirty seconds with arms moving.

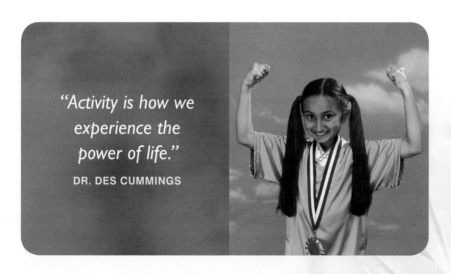

"Activity is how we experience the power of life."

DR. DES CUMMINGS

DISCOVERY

My wife and I settled into "balcony right," row L, seats 26 and 27, and waited for the evening's concert, performed by the Orlando Philharmonic, to begin. For some reason, the preconcert lighting was too dim, so in order to decipher the program notes, I had to hold them about three inches from my face and at just the proper angle to catch a few rays from a small yellowish bulb over my left shoulder. The audience filtered in, and a smattering of musicians on stage practiced sections from various scores.

Eventually the full orchestra was in place and the lights dimmed further. Just as the conductor strode into view, an usher with three people in tow appeared in the aisle to our right. He checked their ticket stubs, then entered two rows in front of us, sliding along, pointing his rather impressive flashlight, and repeatedly offering a monotone, "Excuse me." Well-dressed men and women reacted by either standing to let the rotund, red-jacketed official move past or by pulling their legs up into a kind of modified fetal position.

As the music began, the usher stopped midrow and focused his lens on three already seated attendees, glowering down at them as if they were the perpetrators of some kind of unsavory ruse. He then uttered a command that still echoes in my mind as being every bit as lifesaving as if he were a trained physiologist giving a lecture at Harvard School of Public Health. He told the three incorrectly seated offenders, "You cannot sit there; you'll have to move." That simple phrase, uttered to remedy a simple situation, can actually be used as a wonderful mantra for healthy living in general.

Too many hours in a seated position each day can significantly increase the risk of type-2 diabetes, osteoporosis, cancer, obesity, back and shoulder pain, and varicose veins.

Research has confirmed that none of us should remain seated where we are for very long. Sedentary living is way too hard on our health. We've all got to move. Prolonged sitting has been called the "body's biggest enemy" by *Women's Health* magazine, and a "lethal activity" by *The New York Times*. "Sitting Disease," as it has been labeled, is the direct result of our sedentary jobs and lifestyles.[40]

The list of dangers from extensive sitting is, unfortunately, rather grim. Too many hours in a seated position each day can significantly increase the risk of type-2 diabetes, osteoporosis, cancer, obesity, back and shoulder pain, and varicose veins.[41] The American Cancer Society studied 123,216 people's health over a fourteen-year period and discovered that women who sat more than six hours a day were about 40 percent more likely to die during the study than those who sat less than three hours a day. That number was about 20 percent for men.[42]

In one particularly alarming study, scientists at the Pennington Biomedical Research Center in Louisiana monitored the lifestyles of over seventeen thousand men and women over thirteen years. They discovered that people who sit for most of the day are 54 percent more likely to die of a heart attack![43]

Sitting and watching TV are a common but potentially harmful pairing. According to Australian researchers who followed 8,800 people for six years, a person who watched four hours of TV every day had a whopping 80 percent higher risk of dying from heart disease compared to someone who watched for less than two hours. They were also 46 percent more likely to die from all causes.[44] This link between TV viewing and dramatically increased risk of death "held true regardless of other risk factors such as smoking, poor diet, high cholesterol and obesity."[45]

Also attention getting is the research that indicates that the harmful effects of prolonged sitting *cannot be offset by thirty- to sixty-minute exercise workouts.*[46] The daily trip to the gym is not going to undo the detrimental impact of being immobile the rest of the day. In fact, sitting without taking time to move your muscles can be worse than not exercising.[47]

Authors of the book *Move Yourself* provide this additional insight, "Beginning in 1999 we first reported that physically active overweight people – even those who are obese – are much healthier than their skinnier but sedentary peers."[48] This is serious stuff! Who knew?

My wife and I are fortunate to live less than an hour from Kennedy Space Center on the East Coast of Florida. For me, the most awe-inspiring exhibit at the NASA museum is the Saturn V rocket that sent astronauts to orbit the moon for the first time in December 1968. After two more test flights, the immense vehicle sent Apollo 11 on its way for the first manned lunar landing.

The shuttles, now retired, have all been launched from there since the program's inception. Shuttle astronaut R. Mike Mullane describes the exhilarating experience of weightlessness in his book *Liftoff: An Astronaut's Dream*, when he participated in the 1988 Atlantis mission. He writes about what happened as the vehicle entered the amazing realms of space:

> *On the computer screen I can see the numbers counting down to engine stop ...3 ...2 ...1 ...zero! The crushing force [of gravity] on my chest is instantly gone. The engines are off. They have pushed Atlantis to 25 times the speed of sound or 17,500 miles per hour!*
>
> *I'm weightless! My arms float up. My body floats underneath the seat belt. Tethered checklists float on the ends of cords like snakes rising to a charmer's flute. The drink container that I had used earlier had shaken loose during launch and now it floats in front of my face. I grab it and Velcro® it to the wall.*
>
> *I unsnap my seat belt and remember to use my fingers to propel myself. You have better control with your fingers than with your legs. Most of the time legs are in the way in space. They were designed for walking and you can't do that in weightlessness. About the only thing we use legs for is to hold ourselves steady when we want to work on something. We have canvas loops taped to the floor. By sliding our feet under these loops we can have both hands free. So legs aren't really important.*[49]

Many similarities exist between the ill effects of being in outer space and the adverse impact of prolonged sitting.

NASA has known for some time that space travel can take a toll on an astronaut's health. Several days of weightlessness causes a number of physiological problems such as a decrease in aerobic capacity, slower reaction time, and increased body fat.[50] With the construction of the International Space Station, astronauts are now able to stay in space for months, and the ill effects of non-gravity are much more pronounced.

It turns out that many similarities exist between the ill effects of being in outer space and the adverse impact of prolonged sitting.[51] What is the

The best solution is to vary sitting and standing. The primary focus needs to be on making movement a habit, a way of life.

connection? They both deprive the body of the vital role that gravity plays in maintaining our health and well-being. Both weightlessness and extended sitting here on earth keep the muscles, bones, and other systems from working against gravity, which they are biologically designed to do. Sitting and sedentary living during the day take our muscles off-line, so to speak. They become inactive, and we suffer as a result.

There are many antidotes to prolonged sitting, but the most obvious is to simply stand more.

According to Ray Browning, a Colorado State University professor in the school's Health and Exercise Science department, research shows that muscle contraction and stimulation, which happens naturally in the legs when people are upright, promotes health.[52]

Olivia Judson of the New York Times writes, "Standing in one place is hard work. To stand, you have to tense your leg muscles, and engage the muscles of your back and shoulders; while standing, you often shift from leg to leg. All of this burns energy."[53] Dave Fish, a software engineer, chooses to work while standing at an adjustable desk for part of the day. He says, "I feel more energy. I don't get the afternoon slump after lunch. I feel more productive."[54]

Standing all day creates its own health problems. The Canadian Centre for Occupational Health and Safety states that regularly working in a standing position can cause sore feet, swelling of the legs, varicose veins, low back pain, and other issues.[55] Cashiers, clerks, nurses, factory workers, and other individuals who spend most of their day on their feet are vulnerable.

So the best solution is to vary sitting and standing. If you don't have an adjustable desk, try not to sit for more than forty-five minutes to one hour straight. Take short standing breaks for a minute or two. Getting up slowly and sitting back down slowly compounds the positive impact. As good reminders, set your computer to beep periodically, and make it a practice to stand up whenever you talk on the phone.

Activities of all kinds, big and small, are key.

Also, place some work items you need farther away from your desk so you have to get up to retrieve them.

Don't slouch. Good posture while standing is particularly helpful for your spine. The only weight the top of your spine carries is your head, which can weigh about ten to fifteen pounds. Align your back and neck vertically so the spine carries that full load, which helps maintain bone density. At home, stand up whenever a commercial comes on the TV. For a change, periodically eat standing up. As an adventure, try this routine – pull on your socks and pants and take them off at the end of the day while standing as erect as you can. Be careful! This gets even more interesting if you do it with your eyes shut. This builds your balancing skills that can be compromised by sitting.[56]

Most important is simply moving as much as possible throughout the day.[57] Activities of all kinds, big and small, are key. I'm not talking here about structured workouts. The primary focus needs to be on making movement a habit, a way of life. Sit as little as possible. Swing your arms as you walk. Change positions often. As you go about your daily tasks, take every opportunity you can to stretch, flex, bend, lift, twist, lean, fidget, squat, turn, bow, reach, stoop, duck, and crouch, whether it's putting away groceries or taking the stairs at work.

The author of the book *Sitting Kills, Moving Heals* observes, "If you want to remain healthy and strong for life on Earth, keep doing things, a variety of things, all day, 365 days a year."[58] Beware the chair!

The apostle Paul provides us with a spiritual application by saying that he never allowed himself to sit in one place spiritually. He writes, "I have finished the race, I have kept the faith" (2 Timothy 4:7, NKJV). As he looked back over his eventful life, he was able to report in all humility that he had persistently kept moving forward in his journey with Christ in spite of all the discouragements and roadblocks.

Paul applies the metaphor of running to us as well when he writes, "And let us run with determination the race that lies before us" (Heb. 12:1, GNT). He encourages us not to be motionless in our own spiritual journeys. As we review our lives, we want to be able to say, "I didn't simply sit in one place. I didn't remain stationary in my Christian experience. I ran and kept on running." When we stumbled spiritually, we also got up. When we were derailed, God helped us get back on track. We ran with persistence and kept the faith.

DISCUSSION

Did you ever have a hard time finding the right seat, or have you gotten seated in an unexpected place?

....

....

How often do you intentionally take a break from sitting during the day? What does that break consist of?

....

....

How often do you take a break from standing all day?

....

....

Describe some ways you can make use of TV commercials to become more active.

....

....

How is prolonged sitting like weightlessness? Why is that a problem?

....

....

Would you consider getting an adjustable desk? Why or why not?

....

....

How tired do you feel by late afternoon or suppertime each day? What are some ways such fatigue can be alleviated?

....

....

What was your most important "take away" from this lesson? How can you apply what you have learned this next week?

....

....

SHARING

OPPORTUNITY #3:

- Pray for God to open the way for you to share something from these lessons to help someone else this week.

- Keep your radar up each day for opportunities.

ABUNDANT LIVING THOUGHT

There are many antidotes to prolonged sitting, but the most obvious is to simply stand more.

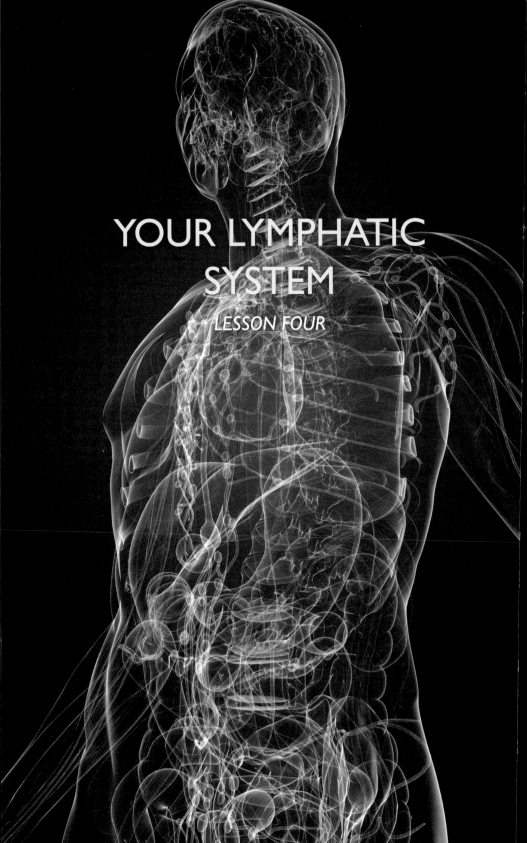

YOUR LYMPHATIC SYSTEM

LESSON FOUR

WARM UP

Feedback: In what ways did God open the door last week for you to share some part of the lessons with someone else?

....

....

....

....

Part A – Choose one or both questions to discuss.

1. Share a story that people have told you about yourself from when you were a baby.[59]

2. What historic person would you like to interview and why?

Part B – Activity Time.

Place your right arm straight out in front of you and allow the wrist to relax downward, fingers extended. Use your left hand to gently pull the right hand toward your body. Now point your hand upward, and again gently pull it toward your body with the other hand. Switch arms and repeat three times.[60] This is a great way to reduce tension in your forearms and wrists.

"Happiness is a state of activity."

ARISTOTLE

DISCOVERY

If you want a Vincent van Gogh painting hanging in your living room, you'll probably have to take out a megaloan. His "Portrait of Dr. Gachet" sold for a cool $82.5 million back in 1990. The "Portrait of Joseph Roulin" brought in $58 million. What you may not know is the famous painter's success was due in large part to his brother Theo, who provided financial support and introduced him to several prominent artists of his day.

Few people know that Marianne Mozart was the older sister of the renowned Wolfgang Amadeus Mozart and that she was originally the big draw playing harpsichord and piano in the early years when the Mozart family went on tour from 1763 to 1766.

Bartholomew Columbus was instrumental in producing the maps that his famous brother Christopher relied on for his historic journeys.

Despite their own personal successes, Theo, Marianne, and Bartholomew all came to play second fiddle to their much better known siblings. Their names have largely dropped from public view.[61]

That same kind of second-fiddle-syndrome has been the sad lot of one of the most important parts of the human body – the lymphatic system. Most people are aware of the circulatory system that carries blood around our bodies and nourishes our many billions of cells. We know about the heart, arteries, veins, bleeding, clotting, scabs, etc. But who knows about the "other" circulatory system that carries around stuff with the weird name "lymph"? We've heard of lymph nodes being removed when someone has cancer, but that's about it. Actually, this much lesser known part of our biology is just as critical as blood flow and entails just as extensive a network.

The lymphatic system is worth exploring for several reasons. For the purposes of this lesson, I want to call attention to it because of the vital role activity and movement play in its healthy operation.

Think of the lymphatic system as being similar to city government with four major departments:

- Transportation
- Water Management
- Police
- Waste Services

TRANSPORTATION

Just like you have little tubes called arteries and veins that carry blood wherever it needs to go, you have just as many other tubes that carry lymph fluid to the same areas. There are some significant differences, however, between the two transport systems. Arteries and veins begin at the heart and reconnect there after traveling throughout the body. Lymph vessels, on the other hand, don't form a complete circuit. They start at one place and end at another without reconnecting, like countless dead end streets winding their way from head to toe among our muscles, organs, and various tissues. Because of special valves, the lymph fluid can only flow in one direction.[62] So the dead-end streets are also one way.

WATER MANAGEMENT

The blood in our cardiovascular system contains the nutrients our cells need, dissolved in blood plasma, which is 90 percent water.[63] On its journey around the body, this nutrient-filled fluid passes out of the arteries and into the surrounding tissues where cells pick up its contents in order to be healthy. Any unused fluid in the tissues is mostly reabsorbed by the capillaries. But about three quarts a day is not.[64] If nothing was done about this leftover fluid and it was allowed to build up, we'd get into serious trouble. First we'd swell up in any affected area, and then our blood levels would drop dangerously low.

It is the job of the lymph system to come to the rescue. It vacuums up the three quarts of leftover fluid that then flows into progressively larger lymphatic vessels, from tiny tubes to much larger trunk lines. It all eventually empties back into the blood through two large veins located near our collar bones.[65] Balance is maintained.

We do not sense it, but a frenetic battle is going on each day at a tiny molecular level inside our bodies that is every bit as dramatic as a bestselling crime novel.

POLICE

We do not sense it, but a frenetic battle is going on each day at a tiny molecular level inside our bodies that is every bit as dramatic as a bestselling crime novel. If we could enlarge and magnify what is going on, it would make a gripping TV series complete with thefts, murders, assaults, 911 calls, manhunts, arrests, fingerprint checks, imprisonment, and executions.

Various types of villains and sleazy characters are running around. We live in a sea of harmful, microscopic bad guys called "antigens." The major ones are bacteria, viruses, microbes, toxins, and ugly-faced parasites. Many come in through what we eat. Thankfully, our saliva and stomach acid put most of them out of commission.[66] Breathing draws in more invaders. Large numbers get trapped in the mucus that lines our nasal passages and are then swallowed. Lots of destructive hordes are also halted by the antibacterial substances secreted by our skin.[67]

One of the ways these bad guys bypass this protection is when we cut ourselves. They rush through the opening like armies excitedly pouring through an ancient city's battered gate. One bacteria can divide to become millions in just a few hours.[68]

You can get some idea of the danger these evil characters pose to us by allowing me to get morbid for a moment. If someone died and was left outside, their immune system would obviously shut down. It would take only a few short weeks for the bacteria, microbes, and parasites to take over and completely dismantle the body until there was nothing left but a skeleton fully picked over like a Thanksgiving turkey.[69]

The lymphatic system plays a major role in fighting off all of these microbial enemies. It is a police force like no other. Just like police take on different roles, from detectives to SWAT team members, so also the lymph system has a variety of enforcers. Here are some of my personal favorites.

Macrophages. The name means "really big eaters."[70] When a macrophage detects a foreign substance, it surrounds it, pulls it inside of itself, and forms a capsule around it. Special enzymes are then inserted into the capsule that digest the offender for lunch. A macrophage actually takes useful parts from the digested intruder and uses them to build itself up.[71]

Killer T-Cells. These cells destroy invaders in two extremely effective ways. One method is to create a hole in the outside of the enemy cell wall which allows water and salts from the surrounding area to enter unabated, compromising the cell's integrity and causing it to eventually burst like an overfilled water balloon.[72] The other method tricks the bad cell into committing suicide. Human cells are preprogrammed to self-destruct when they get old or start acting funky. Killer T-cells activate this preprogramming software in outsiders and then step back and chuckle as the target cells do themselves in.[73] Actor Clint Eastwood's famous line, "Make my day," comes to mind.

Helper T-Cells. These cells emit chemical signals that alert other cells to the danger and activate them. They are the Paul Reveres of the lymphatic system. Helper cells can also grab onto bad guys and yank them over to cells that can destroy them. They are like the little dog that won't let go of the robber's leg until the police arrive.[74]

Memory T-Cells. These cells have the unique ability to remember characteristics of the perpetrators.[75] When the same type of attackers come on the scene again, the memory T-cells don't need to take time to run the name through a lengthy background check. They recognize them instantly and tag them for quick offensive action.[76]

Most of the immune activity of the lymphatic system occurs in small, bean-shaped organs called lymph nodes.[77] Humans have approximately six hundred of these vital nodes, on average, located throughout the body with clusters in the neck, underarms, chest, abdomen, and pelvis.[78] After lymph fluid is examined and filtered by one node, it is passed along to other nodes for additional cleansing of waste and harmful substances. After several such cleansings, the rejuvenated lymph fluid empties back into the bloodstream.

WASTE SERVICES

The lymphatic system also picks up trash from our cells on a regular basis and does away with it. The trash includes such things as cell parts, mutant cells, proteins, bacteria, fats, and dead cells.[79] Red blood cells say goodbye to this world after about 120 days, and white blood cells survive only a few days, on average.[80] So plenty of debris is building up throughout our body for the lymph to cart away.

KEYS TO HEALTHY OPERATION

When the lymphatic system draws in excess fluid, bad guys, and debris, it is critical that the lymph fluid maintain a steady and vigorous flow throughout all of the tubes and nodes. Otherwise its operation and effectiveness would be seriously compromised.

Blood is propelled throughout our cardiovascular system by the heart, which usually beats over four thousand times an hour to push life-giving nutrients out to the cells.

The equally important lymphatic system, however, has no such fist-sized pump. The critical point to understand here is that its primary pump is YOU. When you move, the fluid moves. Physical activity is vital because that's how the system was designed to work. The lymph tubes do create what is called "peristalsis," which are wave-like motions that push contents along.[81] But the system also relies heavily on muscle movement in order to be healthy. Being active on a daily basis makes all the difference.

So what kind of activities do we need to engage in?

1. **Breathe correctly.** When you inhale, your lungs compress the thoracic duct, which is the biggest lymph tube in your body. When you exhale, the vacuum that is created inside the duct pulls in more lymph.[82]

2. **Move frequently.** Simply moving more often throughout the day is immensely helpful. So stand up periodically. Pump your arms and legs. Open and close your fists. Roll your feet around. Turn your head from side to side. Walk more during your daily schedule. The majority of lymph vessels are located just under the skin rather than inside muscles, so even simple movements like yawning, blinking, fidgeting, all of which stretch the skin, are useful.[83]

3. **Do stretching exercises regularly.** The contraction of our muscles helps get lymph liquid from one place to another. When we challenge our muscles, they contract and squeeze the lymph vessels within them, pushing the lymph along like squeezing a toothpaste tube to get toothpaste out.

4. **Use gravity.** If you are on your feet a lot during the day, lymph fluid can tend to gather at the ankles. Reverse that trend by periodically elevating your legs.

5. **Get active right after waking up.** Lymph can pool during sleep when you lie prone for hours. Jump-start lymph flow by stretching before getting out of bed and by doing a few light exercises as soon as you emerge for the day.[84]

Understanding the rudiments of the lymphatic system helps us to realize that *we are designed by God to move.* Our various bodily systems were created with physical activity as one of the design specifications. Without such movement, we live significantly below our potential. So do yourself a huge favor and become more active now.

Jesus talked about another fluid that needs to flow through us in an unimpeded way. On the last day of the annual Jewish Feast of Tabernacles, Christ stood up before the gathered throngs and declared with a loud voice, "Whoever believes in me, as Scripture has said, rivers of living water will flow from within them" (John 7:38, NIV). The "water" is the Holy Spirit, whom God wants to pour into us so he can then flow through us, unobstructed, to bless others. We are designed to be conduits of grace. We are made to be channels of spiritual life and love. The system only works if we cooperate and open our hearts to the Spirit's influence so that God's gracious purposes can be fulfilled.

DISCUSSION

What is the connection between the lymphatic system and activity?

....
....

If you were a body cell applying for a job in the lymphatic system, what task would you select? Why?

....
....

Which of the "enforcers" in the lymph system's police force is your favorite? Why?

....
....

What aspect of the lymphatic system motivates you the most to become more active? Why?

....
....

What one thing could you do to bring more movement and activity into your day?

....
....

How can you remind yourself throughout the day to move more?

....
....

How would you explain the importance of the lymphatic system to a friend?

....
....

Describe when someone served as a "conduit of grace" to you within the last month?

....
....

SHARING

OPPORTUNITY #4:

- Pray for God to open the way for you to share something from these lessons to help someone else this week.

- Keep your radar up each day for opportunities.

ABUNDANT LIVING THOUGHT

Understanding the rudiments of the lymphatic system helps us to realize that we are designed by God to move.

RETHINKING EXERCISE

LESSON FIVE

WARM UP

Feedback: In what ways did God open the door last week for you to share some part of the lessons with someone else?

....
....
....
....

Part A – Choose one or both questions to discuss.

1. What is an activity that lifts your spirits and/or energy level?[85]

2. What is a concern you have about the future?[86]

Part B – Activity Time.

Clasp both hands at the back of your neck. Hold your elbows out wide, squeezing the shoulder blades. Keeping the hands behind your neck, gently bend the head down, then bring your elbows toward each other. Return to original position. Repeat five times.[87]

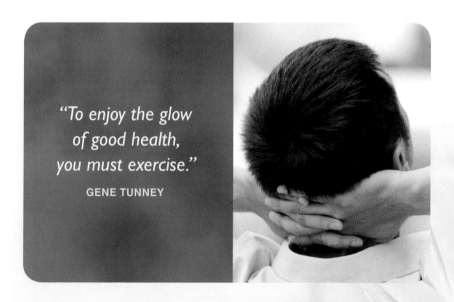

"To enjoy the glow of good health, you must exercise."

GENE TUNNEY

DISCOVERY

There were several health "givens" that I lived with as a child. I never questioned the veracity of these rules because my parents announced them with such conviction and implemented them with unwavering consistency.

For example, "Don't go swimming within an hour of eating." Mom never explained exactly what would happen if I did, so my imagination filled in the blanks. Most of the scenarios I came up with ended with me drowning. This idea is a myth whose origin seems to be the false notion that digestion diverts oxygen away from the muscles used in swimming and toward the stomach.[88]

Another myth was that "getting chilled will give you a cold." I used this concept several times to try and stay home from school. I remember going down to our dank cellar, taking off my shirt, and doing jumping jacks in front of the open door in winter, all in an attempt to get sick. I longed to hear those magic words from my mom, "Sorry to tell you, but it looks like you're too ill to go to school today." No dice. Fact is that we catch colds from infection, not the weather.

I rejected these mistaken beliefs years ago. But some of my biggest misconceptions actually persisted until fairly recently. They had to do with the topic of fitness and exercise.

FIRST MISCONCEPTION – THE DEFINITION OF FITNESS

My concept of fitness used to focus only on aerobic training for my heart and lungs, also called cardio. The problem was that I completely omitted the second and third legs of the fitness stool, strength and flexibility. These are "the big three."

Building *strength* focuses on your skeletal muscles. You don't need to be a weight lifter at the gym. Strength-enhancing activities can include anything that creates resistance that your muscles have to work against. It can range from push-ups to picking up a heavy bag of groceries.

Flexibility is critical to maintaining a full range of motion. Flexibility is important because if you lose it, you can't do many of the activities for cardio and strength.

About four years ago, all of the employees where I work were given a general health screening by a team of experts from a local hospital. It included a test of flexibility. The technician said, "Please get down on the floor. Sit upright and stretch your legs out flat in front of you. Without bending your knees or hunching your back, see how far forward you can reach."

There were at least ten measurement marks on the floor. My mind told my upper torso to lean, but not much happened. I could barely get to the first mark! After I finished embarrassing myself, the technician generously offered, "Good job, Mr. Johnson. That will do."

Alarmed, I have since given much more attention to this third element of the fitness trio. A good resource is *The Complete Idiot's Guide to Stretching* by Barbara and Jamie Templeton.

I have come to understand that a fit person is primarily someone who can engage in a wide range of activities that include cardio, strength, and flexibility. When selecting fitness activities, you need to make sure you are doing something for each of the "big three" in a balanced way.

> *Fitness is a journey that can take us in a variety of directions as we move forward and our understanding increases.*

SECOND MISCONCEPTION – THE PATHS TO FITNESS

My whole concept of *how* to become fit also needed to be revamped, which is represented by the two triangles below.

The left triangle represents my old way of thinking where <u>workouts</u> were the primary way to achieve fitness. By "workout" I mean a set routine of exercises done at a specific time of day for a particular period of time, most often from thirty minutes to an hour. It may involve running, lifting weights, going to a gym, swimming, etc.

On the right is my new way of thinking that is more accurate scientifically. It says that the best way to achieve overall fitness is to focus primarily on developing an active lifestyle throughout the day, with workouts as an additional element to take fitness to the optimal level. Doing both is ideal, but I now know that job #1 should be to develop an active lifestyle where movement permeates my entire day using a variety of activities.

Such a lifestyle, all by itself, will provide very significant health benefits. Deciding to no longer be sedentary and to become more active during the day is a great step forward! *The most important thing is to get moving.* The degree of activity is up to you. Don't ever let an inability to achieve the ideal get in the way of doing something.

The authors of the book *Move Yourself* from the famous Cooper Clinic consider every activity a potential source of fitness. They also write:

> *The tragedy in all of this is that most sedentary people can easily convert their self-destructive "deathstyle" into a healthy lifestyle. We know because we have seen it happen repeatedly. What's more, it can be accomplished with just minutes a day of low-intensity physical activity. That's enough to reap a high dose of benefits – starting within days.* [89]

So what do I mean by an "active lifestyle"? There are two main elements here:

1. Turning "one-fers" into "two-fers."

These terms were coined by the American Heart Association.[90] What they mean is taking a normal daily activity (one-fer) and adding a fitness component to it so it accomplishes two things (two-fer). The task gets done, but you also increase your fitness at the same time.

For example, shopping at the supermarket. Normally you would push the cart around for one purpose only, to fill it with groceries. But if, when you finish shopping, you push the filled cart twice around the inside perimeter of the store before checking out, you add a fitness component and kill two birds with one stone. Those extra laps provide very real health benefits. See the next lesson for more examples.

2. Sprinkling brief periods of exercise throughout your day.

There are many short exercises you can do at home or at the office without detracting from what you need to accomplish. Many people are especially hesitant to add exercises at work. "My schedule is packed already," they complain. That is wrong thinking because introducing more physical activity into your workday will make you more alert, productive, creative, efficient, and help avoid that afternoon slump. You'll actually get more done by periodically taking a few moments for exercise. It also keeps you from being so drained at the end of the day that you have no energy for the evening at home.

These exercises can be done in your work clothes, but it does help to wear comfortable shoes. They can also be done in the privacy of your own office or cubicle and take very little time, in many cases less than a minute. See the next lesson for a list of examples.

THIRD MISCONCEPTION – CARDIO WORKOUTS

The scientific community has come up with some exciting new insights regarding cardio workouts. My thinking used to be that in order to get the best cardio results you had to engage in moderate, repetitive exercises for lengthy periods of time. You had to hit the pavement or the pool or the treadmill, for example, for protracted spans of exertion, up to an hour.

Such activities obviously provide important health benefits and people can engage in them if they want to, but they are no longer necessary in order to receive the same benefits or better.[91]

The great news today about cardio workouts is that they do not have to be lengthy or boring! Researchers have discovered that the best approach is to engage in short periods of intense exertion that leave you winded followed by recovery periods of lower exertion or rest. One period of exertion plus one period of recovery is called a "set." A workout is made up of one or more sets, depending on your level of fitness. These approaches are typically known as "interval training" or "intermittent training."

There are several key principles to keep in mind:

1. **The length of the exertion and recovery periods** will vary depending on the workout plan you choose. Each exertion period can be as short as thirty seconds and each recovery period can be as long as several minutes.[92]

2. **The type of exercise you do** during the exertion period, as well as its length and intensity, needs to vary so that you remain continually challenged. When you are no longer winded or are getting bored, something needs to change.

3. **Any activity qualifies** as long as it can be done vigorously enough that it causes you to get winded and breathe rapidly. Some examples of potential high-intensity workouts are jogging while seated, air boxing, marching in place, doing jumping jacks, and jumping rope.[93] You can also transform any endurance exercise you are currently doing to accommodate these principles.

4. **When you are starting out,** even a few seconds of exercise can leave you gasping for air. You may only be able to do one abbreviated set. That's fine. Begin very slowly and build over time. Be patient and do what is right for your own body. Consult your physician if you have any concerns or health issues.

Rather than outlining a specific cardio workout plan here, I'll point you to a couple of resources so you can study the topic further:

- *The 10-Minute Total Body Breakthrough* by Sean Foy (spiral bound)[94]

- *P.A.C.E.* by Al Sears, MD[95]

Fitness is a journey that can take us in a variety of directions as we move forward and our understanding increases. It is my hope that you will reach out and grasp the fuller life that such a bountiful journey provides.

Jesus certainly had no problem incorporating physical activity into his lifestyle. Until age thirty, he made a living as a carpenter (Mark 6:3). "Carpentry was a rough, tough job that demanded a great deal of physical strength and endurance as well as great skill."[96] They had to cut down trees for lumber to make roof rafters, doors, door frames, window frames, stools, tables, chests, kitchen implements, yokes, plows, shovels, carts, wheels, threshing boards, winnowing forks, and other items.[97]

Christ also did a lot of walking during his lifetime, not as a workout, but as part of the normal lifestyle for the people of his day. Simply traveling to Jerusalem and back for the Jewish feasts each year covered hundreds of miles. During his public ministry, he journeyed between Galilee and Judea many times as well as out to the coast of Phoenicia. The one time we know of when he didn't walk was when he rode a donkey into Jerusalem the Sunday before his crucifixion. In total, he probably walked far more than the equivalent of a trek across the United States and back.[98]

DISCUSSION

Can you recall any additional health myths you grew up with?

....

....

If you had to define "fitness" from what you see on TV commercials, what would that definition be? How does that differ from this lesson?

....

....

Do you feel as strong now as you did five years ago? Why or why not?

....

....

Identify some "one-fers" that you could turn into "two-fers."

....

....

What would be a good way to measure your current degree of flexibility?

....

....

Why does society put so much emphasis on workouts rather than on living an active lifestyle?

....

....

What is one of the most significant changes you have made in your thinking after reading this lesson?

....

....

In what area of your life do you think you could become more physically active? How?

....

....

SHARING

OPPORTUNITY #5:

- Pray for God to open the way for you to share something from these lessons to help someone else this week.

- Keep your radar up each day for opportunities.

ABUNDANT LIVING THOUGHT

A fit person is someone who can engage in a wide range of activities that include cardio, strength, and flexibility.

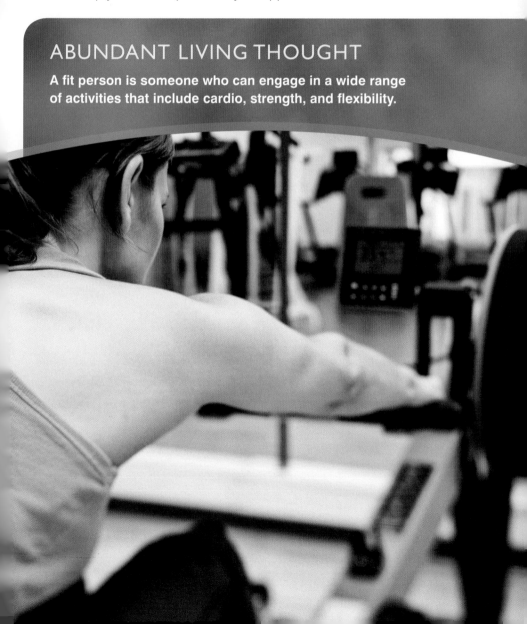

LOTS OF
POSSIBILITIES

LESSON SIX

WARM UP

Feedback: In what ways did God open the door last week for you to share some part of the lessons with someone else?

....

....

....

....

Part A – Choose one or both questions to discuss.[99]

1. Tell about an adventurous experience you have had.

2. Do you consider yourself to be more laid back or more intense? Why?

Part B – Activity Time.

Stand with your arms at your side. Raise both arms overhead and interlace your fingers, palms facing downward. Holding your arms in that overhead position, lean gently to the left and then gently to the right. Do not bounce. Repeat five times.[100]

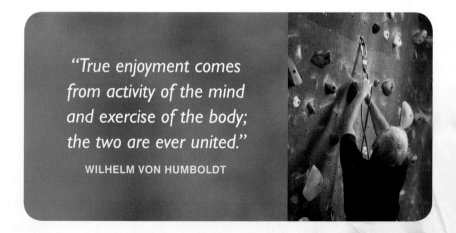

> *"True enjoyment comes from activity of the mind and exercise of the body; the two are ever united."*
>
> **WILHELM VON HUMBOLDT**

DISCOVERY

A significant study conducted by physicians and health professionals from August 1993 through July 1997 compared lifestyle activity versus traditional structured workouts with regard to cardio-respiratory fitness. *The Journal of the American Medical Association* reported their remarkable and very encouraging conclusion, "In previously sedentary healthy adults, a lifestyle physical activity intervention *is as effective* as a structured exercise program in improving physical activity, cardio-respiratory fitness, and blood pressure."[101] Other research has also confirmed the value of an active lifestyle approach.

In this lesson we will delve further into what is meant by an active lifestyle. You recall from the previous lesson that it has two parts: (1) turning "one-fers into two-fers" and (2) incorporating short periods of exercise throughout your day.

Because these topics are not nearly as prominent in people's thinking and awareness as they need to be, I have chosen to provide rather extensive lists in order to be as specific and practical as possible. Hopefully, there are enough examples and suggestions that you can find several items to apply to your life.

ACTIVE LIFESTYLE PART I – TURNING ONE-FERS INTO TWO-FERS

As we learned in the previous lesson, the idea here is to kill two birds with one stone. A "one-fer" is an activity that is already part of your daily routine. You turn it into a "two-fer" by taking that routine activity and adding a fitness component to it. You accomplish the task and improve your fitness at the same time. Our normal activities are not usually fitness oriented, so we need to bump up their fitness value by tweaking and remodeling how they are done. Hopefully, the following lists will serve to spark your imagination so you can add additional ideas. The lists are divided up into home, work, and general.

As you read through the list, highlight those items that you feel have the greatest relevance for you. *The goal at this point is to choose just one new activity from the overall list.* Build that into your routine on a regular basis, and then adopt another one, and so on so that your days become more and more active.[102]

You may wonder how such seemingly small activities can make a difference. It has to do with the principle of "accumulation." Over time, little things add up, especially if they are done consistently. Each of these is a significant improvement over sedentary living. Each one will add to your overall health. No movement is wasted. They're all valuable from an abundant living point of view.[103]

> *Our normal activities are not usually fitness oriented, so we need to bump up their fitness value by tweaking and remodeling how they are done.*

HOME

- Before you get out of bed in the morning, use the mattress as a gym mat to do some stretches. Push your legs away from you, pointing your toes forward. Pull both knees in toward your chin. Repeat.[104]

- While making the bed, walk around it a couple of extra times.

- Do lunges while vacuuming.[105]

- Take fewer grocery bags at a time from the car to the house so you have to make more trips.

- When picking up clothes, do a deep knee bend with each item.

- Any kind of lifting can count as strength training. For example, carefully lift the dirty clothes basket several times.[106]

- Do jumping jacks while waiting for the water to boil on the stovetop.[107]

- Whenever you're at the kitchen sink, put your hands on the edge and do some half push-ups.[108]

- As you brush your teeth in the morning, do deep knee bends, twists, or lean from side to side.[109]

- Ironing is a great activity for the arms and upper body. Before you turn the iron on, hold it out in front of you at shoulder height with each hand for a few seconds. Move it slowly from side to side. Repeat.

- Carry the water for plants instead of using the water hose.[110]

- When you go upstairs, take the stairway twice.

- While watching TV:
  Get up and walk during commercials.
  Stretch as if you are yawning.
  Squeeze a tennis ball.
  March in place.

- Wash your own car instead of going through a car wash.

- If possible, carry your groceries from the store to the car. If you do use a cart, take it back to the corral yourself.[111]

- At your child's sports practices, walk around the field while you wait.[112]

- Take up gardening.

WORK

- Use the stairs instead of the elevator. If you work too many flights up, get off the elevator one or two floors below yours and take the stairs the rest of the way. Same for the way down.[113]

- Use the first step of the stairs as a "stair-stepper." Step up and then back down, alternating legs.

- Stand up for one or two minutes at least once per hour. Do leg lifts, knee bends, and twists.

- Stand up and walk around every time you talk on the phone.

- Hold outdoor "walking meetings" when there are only two or three people involved.

- Take messages to fellow employees personally.

- Do some stretching and leg lifts while waiting for the copy machine to finish your job. You can also do push-ups against the wall.

- Arrive five minutes earlier and stay five minutes later, which allows you to park farther from the building.

- Use the restroom the farthest distance from your office.

- For part of the day at work, sit on a large exercise ball to enhance your core muscles and flexibility.[114]

- Only fill your water bottle halfway, which forces you to get up and refill it more often.

- Put some of the items you need beyond arm's length so you have to walk over and get them.

View any kind of waiting time as a golden opportunity to do exercises.

GENERAL

- Get off the bus one or two stops before your destination and walk the rest of the way.

- View any kind of waiting time as a golden opportunity to do exercises. Simply tighten and release some of your muscles while in the checkout line. While waiting for a dentist or doctor's appointment, tell the receptionist that you'll be in the hallway and to come and get you. Do stretching and flexing.[115] See airport delays as an invitation to take brisk walks.

- Walk in a parking garage. In motels, walk up and down the interior stairway.

- Turn the mall into your own personal gym:

  Do a few laps inside the mall before you start shopping.[116] "Most grocery stores and malls these days are huge. Here's a shopping mall trick that sounds crazy but works. In between each store in which you browse, you must walk at least five hundred steps or one full lap of the mall before you enter the next store. Count them out one hundred at a time. Walk briskly... right past that Cinnabon."[117]

  Climb the stairs inside the mall rather than taking the escalator. If the stairs are too difficult, walk up the escalator rather than just passively riding.

- Get active while driving:[118]
  Grip the steering wheel extra tightly and release.
  Move your neck back and forth periodically without losing concentration.
  Sit up straight.
  Do shoulder shrugs.

- Take advantage of stopped traffic to practice deep breathing. Take some hand weights along and do some pumps at each red light.[119]

- Park in a spot farthest from your destination. It'll be easier to find a spot!

- Walk into the bank rather than using the drive-up window.[120]

ACTIVE LIFESTYLE PART 2 – SPRINKLING BRIEF PERIODS OF EXERCISE THROUGHOUT YOUR DAY

You can do scores of brief exercises during the day without interfering with your schedule. Here are a few examples to get you started. When doing an exercise using a chair, make sure it is firmly in place and won't roll out from under you.

STRENGTHENING

- Wall Push-up – Stand about two feet from a sturdy wall with legs slightly apart. Place your hands on the wall at about shoulder height. Keep your body straight and lean forward until your nose almost touches the wall. Push back out until your arms are straight. Repeat.[121]

- Wall Sit – While standing, place your back against a wall with your heels about two feet out from the wall. Bend your knees and lower your upper body slowly until you are in a seated position, back still against the wall. Hold for ten seconds, then stand. Repeat up to five times.[122]

- Cubicle Ab Challenge – Sit in a sturdy chair. Feet on the floor, place each hand on the seat next to your torso. Grasping the seat firmly, lift your hips up off the seat while tightening your abdomen. Repeat up to thirty seconds total.[123]

STRETCHING

- Upper Back Stretch – Sit upright in a chair, keeping your feet on the floor. Place your right hand on the outside of your left knee, then turn your torso to the left until you feel a stretch between your shoulder blades. Repeat on the other side.[124]

- Neck Rolls – Sit on the front of your chair, with good posture. Tilt your head forward, backward, and then side to side. Do it slowly and only as much as is comfortable.[125]

- Chair Sit-Ups – From a seated position, put your feet next to each other on the floor and then place your hands behind your head. Bend forward toward the knees, then return to a regular sitting position. Repeat five to ten times.[126]

- Leg Lifts – While seated, lift your left leg with knee bent ten times and repeat with the right leg.[127]

The following books are great resources for strength and flexibility:

Deskercise! by Dr. Todd M. Berntson,
Center Path Media, Inc., Apple Valley, MN, 2005

Fitness 9 to 5, by Shirley Archer,
Chronicle Books, San Francisco, CA, 2006

Get Fit While You Sit, by Charlene Torkelson,
Hunter House Publishing, Alameda, CA, www.hunterhouse.com

Fitting In Fitness, American Heart Association,
Clarkson Potter/Publishers, New York, NY.

> *You can do scores of brief exercises during the day without interfering with your schedule.*

Remember, the key is doing something.

For most people in Jesus's day, their normal daily activities required fitness. For example, four of Jesus disciples were fishermen – Peter and his brother Andrew, plus James and his brother John. They had their own boats and lived in Bethsaida and Capernaum. They were experienced in various methods of fishing. When Jesus called Peter and Andrew to follow him, they were in the shallows casting nets that were about fifteen feet in diameter (Matt. 4:18). In Matthew 17:24–27 we read that Peter caught a fish by using a hook and line. All four disciples also used nets from their boats in the Sea of Galilee (Mark 1:16). If we saw them, they would likely appear trim, muscular, and very fit, with impressive stamina.

"The greatest benefits come from raising yourself up a notch from low-fitness status to moderate fitness – going from doing nothing to doing something, even if it's just a minimum amount of activity." [128]

DISCUSSION

Which items in "Active Lifestyle Part 1" are people in the group already doing? Describe.

....

....

What activity from Part 1 under "Home" could you *add* to your routine?

....

....

What activity from Part 1 under "Work" could *add* to your routine?

....

....

What activity from Part 1 under "General" could *add* to your day?

....

....

What would it take for you to start parking farther from your destinations?

....

....

What could you do to become more active during TV commercials?

....

....

What new exercise from "Active Lifestyle Part 2" could you start doing in the next few days?

....

....

Which of the activities in this lesson do you think would benefit you the most?

....

....

....

SHARING

OPPORTUNITY #6:

- Pray for God to open the way for you to share something from these lessons to help someone else this week.

- Keep your radar up each day for opportunities.

ABUNDANT LIVING THOUGHT

You can take a routine activity and add a fitness component to it.

IMMEDIATE BENEFITS

LESSON SEVEN

WARM UP

Feedback: In what ways did God open the door last week for you to share some part of the lessons with someone else?

....

....

....

....

Part A – Choose one or both questions to discuss.

1. What is some of the best advice you have received about how to relieve stress?[129]

2. Looking back on your high school years, what do you wish you had done that you didn't?[130]

Part B – Activity Time.

Stand up with arms at your side. Keeping your back straight, bend your knees slightly and hold for ten seconds, then straighten. Repeat four times.[131]

> *"A man's health can be judged by which he takes two at a time – pills or stairs."*
>
> **JOAN WELSH**

DISCOVERY

The sign at the beginning of the trail read:

"STOP. The area ahead has the worst weather in America. Many have died there from exposure even in the summer. Turn back <u>NOW</u> if the weather is bad.

WHITE MOUNTAIN NATIONAL FOREST."

Our family simply called it the "Many have died" sign. Along with five million other visitors each year, the hefty warning never deterred us from climbing the magnificent, lofty mountains of New Hampshire's Presidential Range.[132] We tackled heights that varied from 3,500 to over 4,500 feet through thick forest and over large boulders when we emerged above tree line.

The trail was marked with patches of white, red, blue, or yellow paint brushed on conspicuous trees at various intervals. We occasionally caught glimpses of the peak looming above us as we meandered through dry river beds, over roots, and along leaf-strewn paths. We were spurred on by the goal of reaching the summit and eating lunch while enjoying an unobstructed, 360 degree view of the other peaks and the distant, multicolored valley below.

But the peak was not our only incentive. In many ways our family was drawn more by the experiences we knew we would invariably have on the way to the top:

- The sounds of birch leaves rustling in the breeze.
- Dappled sunlight dancing on the forest floor.
- Birds calling out in song and warning.
- Little critters scurrying for cover.
- The towering pines, sprawling maples, and elegantly formed oaks.
- Lichen-draped rock formations that created mini-caves and took on odd shapes resembling modern art in 3D.
- The intoxicating smell of opening buds, moist moss, and rotting leaves.
- Relatively short, but always challenging, hand-over-hand vertical scrambles.

If the only benefit the mountains offered was reaching the top, we would not have hiked nearly as often as we did. It was both that distant goal and the short-term benefits along the way that kept us coming back for more. We needed the payoffs from both the journey's end and the journey itself to keep us motivated.

So it is with activity and exercise. There are the long-term benefits of avoiding cardiovascular disease, lowering the risk of cancer, stroke, dementia, osteoporosis, diabetes, etc. These are obviously important but usually show up quite a distance down the road. The problem is that most people need other, short-term benefits to get them to adopt an active lifestyle and keep them motivated. Life is so pressing and schedules are so packed that unless an endeavor has immediate results, we tend to put it off. Like mountain climbing, we need the lure of both the distant and the close at hand.

Many people are unaware that numerous benefits accrue right away from an active lifestyle. No need to wait years or even decades. The following is a list of some of the immediate impacts that activity and exercise can have on our life just as soon as we do them. They can enhance our living on a daily basis. The motivating power of these quick returns can help us get moving now rather than putting it off until later.

1. We have more material for making bricks to hold back the tide.

When you build a sand castle at the beach by shaping the walls and carving out the windows and parapets, you know that your creation will not last forever. You can hear the oncoming sea in the background, but you are initially so consumed with constructing your fortress that it

does not consciously affect your joy. As the waves get closer, however, they begin to intrude more and more on your thinking. So you build a moat. Then a bigger moat. Later, just as you step onto the parking lot to leave, you cast a glance back at the castle and see the ocean-facing wall begin to crumble.

That castle represents our life. The tide represents serious illness and death that will one day come our way. Exercise enables us to build a bulwark against that tide. Each time we exercise, we receive more material to build a solid brick wall between ourselves and the inevitable. As time goes by, the wall gets thicker and higher. We push back the timeline of our own health problems and demise. On the other hand, every time we neglect to exercise, we have fewer wall-making materials to work with. Neglecting exercise today directly affects the size of the bulwark we are able to construct over time against the inexorable, incoming tide.

2. Less heartburn.[133]

3. Building healthier skin.

If you didn't exercise today, you missed an opportunity to have better-looking skin. We slough off gobs of old skin cells every day and they need to be replaced. Regular activity builds new cells that glow. Lack of exercise… not so much.

"We tend to focus on the cardiovascular benefits of physical activity, and those are important. But anything that promotes healthy circulation also helps keep your skin healthy and vibrant," says dermatologist Ellen Marmur, MD, author of *Simple Skin Beauty: Every Woman's Guide to a Lifetime of Healthy, Gorgeous Skin* and associate professor of dermatology at Mount Sinai School of Medicine.[134]

4. Improved sleep.

A large study published in the journey *Mental Health and Physical Activity* revealed that moderate exercise increases the participant's sleep quality by 65 percent over their sedentary peers.[135] Activity can save you a trip to the pharmacy for a sleep aid. Better sleep, in turn, brings with it a whole host of daily benefits. If you simply sat around all of today, you most likely lost the opportunity for a better snooze tonight.

5. Reduced snoring.[136]

6. Fewer migraines.

According to the Migraine Research Foundation, approximately 36 million people in the United States suffer from migraines which results in over a hundred million lost work days each year. The intense pain, usually in one side of the head, can produce nausea, vomiting, and increased sensitivity to light and sound. Findings indicate that physical activity can at times serve to prevent migraines just as well as medication.[137]

Sand castles represent life, and exercise enables us to build a bulwark against the coming tide.

7. Stave off flu and colds.

If you are choosing inactivity, you are missing a great chance to keep the flu and colds at bay. You could have given your immune system a real boost today. Instead, you just increased your chances of a getting a runny nose and sore throat by at least one third. You may be getting a sincere "thank-you" card from some stray bacteria or virus that just entered your system.

David Nieman, PhD, a professor in the department of health and exercise science at Appalachian State University in Boone, North Carolina, found that people who exercise regularly have half the number of colds and sore throats than less active individuals.[138]

8. Feel more upbeat and happy.

Physical activity causes the release of feel-good chemicals in our brain that make us happier and more optimistic during the day.[139] Penn State researcher Amanda Hyde says, "Doing more exercise than you typically do can give you a burst of pleasant-activated feelings. So today, if you want a boost, go do some moderate-to-vigorous intensity exercise."[140] Physical activity also has a positive effect on depression, anger, and stress.[141] If you chose to be sedentary today, you missed a great opportunity to feel better all day.

9. Increase your sex drive.

Our sex drive depends on a number of factors, including hormones. The sex drive hormone for both men and women is testosterone, which is increased by physical activity. Moreover, exercise raises blood flow, which is another key ingredient for healthy sexual function for both genders.[142]

10. Allow the heart to work less.

Every day a heart that lives inside the chest of a person who is fit will beat much less than a heart that dwells within a sedentary individual.[143] Suppose that through becoming active you are able to slow your resting heartbeat from 75 beats a minute to 70. That is a saving of 7,200 beats a day and a staggering 2,628,000 beats a year! How long do you want *your* heart to last?

11. Turbo-charge capillaries.

As we move our large muscle groups, they demand more oxygen. In turn, the tiny capillaries in our cardiovascular system happily expand to provide a greater flow of blood to the area. They also carry away more waste.[144] If your capillaries could dial your cell phone each morning, they'd undoubtedly say something like, "Hey, get moving, buster."

12. Burn calories to avoid weight gain.

Not only does exercise use up calories and keep the pounds off, it can also help people move off of a weight loss plateau.[145]

13. Increase your energy.[146]

Authors Ted Mitchell, MD, and Tim Church, MD, PhD, write, "Sedentary living robs you of energy. Physical activity brings it back and reduces fatigue. It's as simple as that. On the surface you might think it would work the opposite, that activity would make you more tired. If you think that way, you are buying into a persistent myth."[147]

If your capillaries could dial your cell phone each morning, they'd undoubtedly say something like, "Hey, get moving, buster."

14. Enhance brainpower.
Because activity delivers more oxygen and nutrients to the brain, you can concentrate better and think more clearly throughout the day.[148]

15. Better digestion and elimination.[149]

16. Improve total cholesterol.[150]
Your HDL "good" cholesterol is increased, which has a protective effect on the heart, and your LDL "bad" cholesterol decreases, lowering the chances of a heart attack or stroke.

17. Make your heart and lungs more efficient.[151]
Giving these organs a good workout strengthens them and makes them more efficient. You build up reserve capacity as a safety buffer.

18. Produce greater joint flexibility.[152]
Inactivity causes our muscles, ligaments, and tendons to weaken, creating imbalances, misalignments, and a domino effect throughout the musculoskeletal system. Even moderate activity starts immediately to correct the problem by strengthening tissues that support the skeleton and joints.[153]

19. Enhance the body's use of blood sugar.[154]
Activity increases your insulin sensitivity, which means that more glucose will get into the cells rather than remaining in the bloodstream. This puts a smile today on the face of your cells and your pancreas as well.[155]

20. Boost your self-confidence.[156]
Achieving fitness goals instills confidence that spills over into other areas of life.

> *Boost your self-confidence.*
> *Achieving fitness goals*
> *instills confidence that spills over*
> *into other areas of life.*

The authors of the book *Move Yourself* write, "Our research says that however long you have to live, every day of your life will be far better if you are involved in physical activity."[157]

Considering the bucket load of immediate benefits regular activity brings, the comment from Marilyn Moffat, a professor of physical therapy at New York University, appears to be right on target, "Even if exercise is tough to schedule," Dr. Moffat said, "you feel so much better, it's crazy not to do it."

In the Bible, Psalm 118:24 reads, "This is the day the Lord has made; we will rejoice and be glad in it" (NKJV). The more we can focus on today instead of rehearsing regrets from yesterday or worries about tomorrow, the better off we'll be mentally and emotionally. The same can be true of fitness. Rather than berating ourselves for lack of exercise in the past or putting action off until a "better day," we have the privilege of taking advantage of all the benefits of physical activity that are available on the best of all days called today.

DISCUSSION

Would you rather have $100 today or $1,000 in three years? Why?

....

....

Name one of the twenty immediate benefits of activity that was new to you?

....

....

Which of the immediate benefits would appeal the most to young people? Why?

....

....

Which of the immediate benefits do you personally find most motivating? Why?

....

....

Are there any immediate benefits of activity that you could add to the list?

....

....

Why are short-term benefits more motivating than long-term ones?

....

....

What are some keys to sustaining short-term motivations over a lifetime?

....

....

If you were to write a book to motivate people to adopt a more active lifestyle, what would the title be?

....

....

....

SHARING

OPPORTUNITY #7:

- Pray for God to open the way for you to share something from these lessons to help someone else this week.

- Keep your radar up each day for opportunities.

ABUNDANT LIVING THOUGHT

Many people are unaware that numerous benefits accrue right away from an active lifestyle.

BEYOND
GOOD INTENTIONS

LESSON EIGHT

WARM UP

Feedback: In what ways did God open the door last week for you to share some part of the lessons with someone else?

....

....

....

....

Part A – Choose one or both questions to discuss.

1. If studying in a group, what is one of the most memorable experiences you've had during the group meetings?

2. What one thing do you plan to do after these lessons are over to become more active?

Part B – Activity Time.

Stand with arms at your sides. Shrug both shoulders up toward your ears. Hold for five seconds, then relax the shoulders. Tilt your head first to the left and then to the right. Bring back to center. Repeat five times.[158]

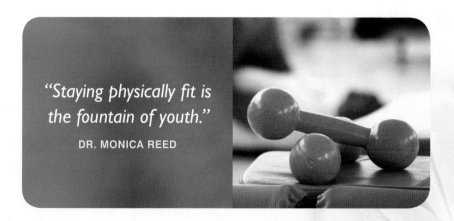

"*Staying physically fit is the fountain of youth.*"

DR. MONICA REED

DISCOVERY

I had no doubt that one day I would be monetarily rich. I just had to find the right scheme to get me there.

Successful entrepreneurs say you should find a need in society and fill it. My first attempt to do just that was an invention I tentatively called "Sock Sense." You have most likely endured the aggravation of putting ten socks into the dryer and later only being able to find nine. Where in the world does the tenth sock go? It happens time and time again. I never lose shirts or pants or underwear. Just socks. One time I poked my head inside the still warm dryer drum and scanned the circular bandit with the thoroughness of a CSI agent. No luck.

I have come to two solid conclusions. First, socks are escapist by nature. It's embedded into their DNA. They are never happy where they are and always harbor this unwarranted wanderlust. Secondly, socks are extremely ungrateful. I am consistently kind to my socks. Knowing their tendency to disappear, I treat them with great respect and tenderness. I wash them with detergents that have no harsh chemicals and dry them at safe temperatures. But still they flee.

I intended to design a method for holding sock pairs together when you put them in the washer and then in the dryer. A clip, a band, a hole for inserting one sock into the other – I had a half a dozen possibilities. The company that would make this stunning invention would rake in piles of money from an appreciative public. Problem was I always intended to follow through but never did, and because I most likely never will, I'm sharing this gem of an idea now with you.

Intentions can be fun, exciting, and, to some degree, satisfying. But they are no substitute for actually doing something. If people could become fit mentally and physically by simply intending to do so, the whole world would be in great shape. It is the aggravating gap between intention and action that is at the root of so much unfitness in our society.

My purpose here is not to make you feel guilty. The goal is to offer suggestions about how to turn fitness intentions into firm reality. The following sections explore how to actually get moving and become more active.

1. Acknowledge our humanness.

During my sedentary years I comforted myself with what I might call the "Not Me Syndrome." I adopted an attitude of immunity from the big, bad stuff that medical reports said people who weren't active could suffer. I wasn't oblivious. There was a tiny voice in the back of my head that said, "Hey, you could get one of those health problems." I just made sure that the volume was turned down low on that track and cranked up high on the track labeled "denial."

Did I think I was some kind of superman, blessed with perpetual immunity? Sure, my best friend had to have a quintuple heart bypass, but there were certainly key differences between us. He ate a lot of spicy food and I didn't. He wore tight shirts and I didn't. He lived up north and I didn't. He was a full two years older than me. Or, to put it another, more compelling way, seven hundred and thirty days older. He was bald and I wasn't. I was grasping here, of course, but anything to avoid taking action.

I have finally broken through such magical thinking. I now feel my humanity, my vulnerability. I don't morbidly obsess, but I fully acknowledge that unhappy things could occur unless I get off my backside. With this more honest perspective, I have become more focused, more earnest, more committed to living an active life.

2. Periodically look backward.

Motivational speakers will often say, "Always keep your eye on the goal." To be honest, when it comes to activity and exercise, that doesn't work so well for me. There is certainly real value in paying attention to future possibilities and goals. But I also recommend periodically looking back as well. Rather than spending all my time looking at how much further I have to go, it can be very motivating to see how far I've already come.

It's kind of like rowing. During my growing up years, our family lived near the sea. Learning how to swim and row were givens. The only people who couldn't were the tourists, who us year-rounders called "summer complaints."

Learning to row could be frustrating until you have figured out how to pull equally on both oars. Otherwise you'd spend an hour or so going in circles. A rower regularly peers over their shoulder to make sure they aren't headed out into open ocean, but they also look back at how far they've traveled.

Applying that concept to activity, no matter how little activity you've done, by taking time to look backward you can always say, "I'm not where I used to be." And feeling good about yourself is the vital emotional fuel you need to keep on pulling.

3. Stick with it so you experience the benefits.

Imagine a man named Frank who longs to raise his own tomatoes. He wants to go more organic and can almost taste the juicy slices in a bulging sandwich with low-fat mayo. So he laboriously digs up an eight-foot by four-foot plot in his backyard, adds fertilizer, and plants seeds for both cherry and beefsteak tomatoes. He then waters the soil thoroughly. It is the perfect location with at least eight hours of full sun.

The next morning he rushes out before work to check his precious investment. Nothing happening so far. The second morning he hurries out, gets down on his knees, leans over, and inspects the area closely, but no change. Frank reenters the house frustrated. Third day, nothing. *Could the seeds be defective?* he questions. Fourth day, nothing. Our first-time gardener is visibly upset. Fifth day, no evidence of life, and Frank is sure he's been taken. "A waste of good money!" he snorts. Day six and not a thing showing, so he grabs a shovel and in a fit of anger turns over all the soil and never utilizes the plot again.

An onlooker would surely say, "You're too impatient. Keep at it and the vegetables will come. Give it time." Frank's expectations were clearly unrealistic, and the same can happen to would-be exercisers. Unless there are obvious, discernible results, we throw in the towel. But if we just hang in there and don't quit too early, the benefits will emerge.

Keeping at it until we reap the benefits is crucial because it is those perceived gains that will sustain you for the long term. At first we choose to adopt a more active lifestyle because we know intellectually that it is good for us. It is a matter of willpower. But willpower is an expendable commodity and eventually wears out. What needs to kick in at that point is the joy of experiencing fruits from our efforts. But if we bail out too soon, that extra boost will never be realized.

> *Intentions can be fun, exciting, and, to some degree, satisfying. But they are no substitute for actually doing something.*

4. Decide how abundant you want your life to be.

Many people settle for less than they can have. Due to inadequate role models, low self-esteem, or other causes, they come to accept a level of wellness, energy, and fitness that is well below what is available.

Imagine a parent who wins a free shopping spree in a large supermarket. They are poor and struggling to feed five hungry children. The prize allows them to take out as much food as they can haul in thirty minutes. The big day arrives, the parent stands ready at the front of the store with an empty shopping cart in hand. News crews snap photos. The whistle blows, and the parent dashes into the store, races over to the pasta section, grabs a single box of spaghetti, runs out, and declares, "I'm done."

That odd scenario is not far from what some people do with their physical and mental well-being. So much is available, yet so little is taken. God is eager for you to grab all the abundant living possible. Don't settle for a box of pasta when you could overflow the cupboards.

5. Take very small steps.

The number one reason for failure in the pursuit of a more active lifestyle is attempting to do too much too soon. People get discouraged, then they stop. But something, no matter how small, done consistently, is always better than nothing. For instance, standing and moving a little once an hour instead of sitting throughout the day is a great step forward. Taking the stairs instead of the elevator is a great step forward. How small should each activity goal be? Small enough that you can't help but do it.

6. Build in variety.

Anyone gets bored doing the same thing over and over. So in order to keep your interest up, you need to vary the elements of your new active lifestyle. Whenever your commitment starts to flag, that is a clear sign that it is time to switch gears and introduce some new challenge or new activity into your days. Rekindle your enthusiasm by trying something you've never done before. Experiment, explore, reach further, spend more time in play.

7. Honor God's gift.

Several years ago, the television program *Antiques Roadshow* came to the quaint Scottish town of Ayrshire. A woman showed the appraiser the glass bowl she had retrieved from her attic for the occasion. The lady and her husband had originally purchased it at a yard sale for one English pound. She said, "We bought it for the plant because it looked nice in the bowl." Later they figured it was just a piece of junk and almost tossed it in the trash.

The antique expert, Eric Knowles, was stunned. He said: "I've been waiting over twenty-five years for such a piece to come in to a *Roadshow* and this was the stuff of dreams." The owners later sold the bowl at an auction with Christie's for what would currently be over $50,000 US.[159]

We may look at our bodies as being quite ordinary, but, like the bowl, they are in fact extremely valuable. The Scriptures tell us, "Do you not know that your bodies are temples of the Holy Spirit, who is in you, whom you have received from God? You are not your own; you were bought at a price. Therefore honor God with your bodies" (1 Cor. 6:19–20, NIV). We are doubly valuable because (1) we are indwelt by the Holy Spirit and (2) God purchased us with the sacrifice of his Son.

Because our bodies are so important to God, it behooves us to treat them with enormous respect and care for them with a deep sense of gratitude.

Imagine how precious a donated heart is to a man whose own heart is failing. Imagine how priceless a donated kidney is to a lady who is on life-preserving dialysis. Imagine the thrill someone would feel to get two donated lungs when his own have been decimated by disease. Most of us already have an incredible heart, two fantastic kidneys, and two extraordinary lungs, plus all our other healthy organs. View what you have with the same degree of thankfulness and appreciation as someone would who is in desperate need.

We are an amazing biological collection of God-given gifts. As the Psalmist has written, "I praise you because I am fearfully and wonderfully made" (Psalm 139:14, NIV). Now is a wonderful time to rededicate ourselves to keeping our body-temple in great working order for the Creator's sake as well as our own.

You *can* become a more active person. You *can* move more. Take the seven points in this lesson to heart and make a start. If you have already started, move your activity level up a notch or two. Keep at it. You are more than worth it. You certainly deserve to give yourself the best.

"Why wait to be sick before you decide to be well?"[160]

DISCUSSION

Describe invention ideas you had that didn't pan out or you never tried.

....

....

What usually keeps you from following through on good intentions?
How can that be overcome?

....

....

Tell of a time when looking backward boosted your confidence after
seeing how far you'd come.

....

....

What kind of benefits from your fitness journey would help the most to
keep you motivated?

....

....

Describe some of the reasons why you want your life to be more
abundant and fulfilling.

....

....

As you look back over this set of lessons, what specific insights have
you found to be most helpful? Why?

....

....

What one or two goals can you set for yourself in developing a more
active lifestyle? What is your timeline for achieving them?

....

....

What small step can you take this coming week toward accomplishing
your activity goals?

....

....

SHARING

OPPORTUNITY #8:

- Pray for God to open the way for you to share something from these lessons to help someone else this week.

- Keep your radar up each day for opportunities.

ABUNDANT LIVING THOUGHT

Rather than spending all my time looking at how much further I have to go, it can be very motivating to see how far I've already come.

ABOUT THE AUTHOR

Kim Johnson is a popular writer, speaker, and fervent advocate for holistic living. As the author of three books, eleven lesson series, and many articles, his writings focus on healthy living and spiritual connectedness. His materials have been used in hundreds of churches throughout North America and internationally as well.

Johnson is an ordained minister with more than 35 years of experience as a parish pastor and church administrator. Over the years, his work with parishioners emphasized principles of whole-person health as a path to optimum mental, physical, social, and spiritual well-being. His later work with pastors and church leaders emphasized skill development such as vision casting, goal setting, support systems, relationship management, and accountability. Johnson has put his experience of working with pastors and parishioners to use in the CREATION Health Life Guide Series by creating a resource ideally suited for use in churches, small groups or individual study.

Johnson holds a Master of Divinity degree and received his Bachelor of Arts in theology. He currently serves as Director of Resource Development for churches in the state of Florida. His personal interests include reading, classical music, art and book festivals, kayaking, traveling, volunteering, and small group study. He and his wife Ann make their home in Orlando.

Author Acknowledgements: It has been a great privilege for me to be associated with the team of dedicated individuals who helped in various ways to make these CREATION Health Life Guides available. I would like to single out my wife Ann and daughter Stefanie, whose feedback and suggestions were always characterized by unfailing support and clear-eyed honesty. I have also received invaluable guidance and encouragement from Mike Cauley, Tim Nichols, Nick Howard, and Jim Epperson. Finally, I want to thank the group of local pastors who met with me personally and provided a wonderful forum for evaluating the lesson drafts.

NOTES

1. Garry Poole, *The Complete Book of Questions* (Grand Rapids, MI: Zondervan, 2003), 47, 76.

2. Chris Maslanka and David Owen, *Neurobics* (Pleasantville, NY: Reader's Digest, 2010), 47.

3. Daniel Coyle, *The Talent Code* (New York, NY: Bantam Book, 2009), 215.

4. "Study Peeks at How Our Brains Grow," Lauran Neergaard, *USA Today*, May 18, 2007, http://www.usatoday.com/tech/science/discoveries/2007-05-18-brain-growth_N.htm.

5. Lawrence C. Katz, PhD, Manning Rubin, *Keep Your Brain Alive* (New York, NY: Workman Publishing Company, 1999), 18.

6. Katz and Rubin, *Keep Your Brain Alive*, 5.

7. "Steps to a Nimble Mind: Physical and Mental Exercise Help Keep the Brain Fit," Kathleen Phalen Tomaselli, Amednews.com, November 17, 2008, http://www.ama-assn.org/amednews/2008/11/17/hlsa1117.htm.

8. Katz and Rubin, *Keep Your Brain Alive*, 34.

9. Katz and Rubin, *Keep Your Brain Alive*, 33.

10. "Mental Exercise for a Better Brain," The Franklin Institute Online, accessed November 3, 2012, http://www.fi.edu/learn/brain/exercise.html#mentalexercise.

11. "Neurobics: Exercising Your Brain," Timothy Sexton, Yahoo!Voices, May 10, 2006, http://voices.yahoo.com/neurobics-exercising-brain-34365.html?cat=5.

12. "Steps to a Nimble Mind," Tomaselli, http://www.ama-assn.org/amednews/2008/11/17/hlsa1117.htm.

13. Katz and Rubin, *Keep Your Brain Alive*, 15–16.

14. Ibid., 6.

15. Ibid., 24.

16. Ibid., 42.

17. Ibid., 28.

18. "Steps to a Nimble Mind," Tomaselli, http://www.ama-assn.org/amednews/2008/11/17/hlsa1117.htm.

19. Barbara Ann Kipfer, *4,000 Questions for Getting to Know Anyone and Everyone* (New York, NY: Random House Reference, 2004), 23, 82.

20. "Music and Movement - Instrumental in Language Development," Maryann Harman, Early Childhood News, accessed November 3, 2012, http://www.earlychildhoodnews.com/earlychildhood/article_view.aspx?ArticleID=601; Alice H. Cash, "What Can the Unborn Baby Hear?" Blogspot.com, September 5, 2009, http://pregnancyandpreemies.blogspot.com/2009/09/what-can-unborn-baby-hear.html.

21. "Rutgers-Newark Researchers Link Early Movement, Brain Development," Eureka Alert.org, accessed November 3, 2012, http://www.eurekalert.org/pub_releases/2004-12/rtsu-rrl122004.php; "Prenatal Development – The Dana Guide," Ann McDonald, The Dana Guide, November 2007, http://www.dana.org/news/brainhealth/detail.aspx?id=10050; "Physical Movement Opens the Door to Brain Growth and Development," Moira Dempsey and Julia Morgan, Dumex, accessed November 3, 2012, http://www.dumex.com.sg/young_children/child_development/article/physical_movement_opens_the_door_to_brain_growth_and_development.

22. "Crawling and Creeping for Healthy Brain Development," A4everFamily. org, accessed November 3, 2012, http://www.a4everfamily.org/index. php?option=com_content&task=view&id=202&Itemid=108; "Our Amazing Babies Movement and the Developing Brain," Cathrine Burns, MLRC, accessed November 3, 2012, http://www.themlrc.org/enewsletter/feb2008/0108movement. htm; "Brain Development in Babies Who Take Longer to Walk," Heather Robson, eHowMom, accessed November 3, 2012, http://www.ehow.com/about_6694635_ brain-development-babies-longer-walk.html.

23. "Brain Development," Play 2 Grow, accessed November 3, 2012, http://www. play-2-grow.com/research.htm.

24. "Movement," Terry Sweeting, PhD, accessed November 3, 2012, http://www. aplaceofourown.org/question_detail.php?id=663.

25. "Train Your Brain With Exercise," Jean Lawrence, WebMD, accessed November 3, 2012, http://www.webmd.com/fitness-exercise/guide/ train-your-brain-with-exercise.

26. "Fun Facts About The Brain," Brain Health & Puzzles, accessed November 3, 2012, http://www.brainhealthandpuzzles.com/fun_facts_about_the_brain.html.

27. Ibid.

28. John J. Ratey, MD, *Spark* (New York, NY: Little, Brown and Company, 2008), 234.

29. "Lifestyle Tips," FitBrains, accessed November 3, 2012, http://www.fitbrains. com/lifestyle/; "Exercise and the Brain: It Will Make You Want to Work Out," Len Kravitz, accessed November 3, 2012, http://www.unm.edu/~lkravitz/Article%20 folder/brainandex.html.

30. Ratey, *Spark*, 76; "The Effects of High Cortisol," John Zaremba, eHow.com, last updated April 10, 2012, http://www.ehow.com/list_5960002_effects-high-cortisol. html; "Amygdala and Cortisol," Matthew Busse, Livestrong.com, June 11, 2010, http://www.livestrong.com/article/146203-amygdala-and-cortisol/; "Stress: Your Brain and Body," Your Amazing Brain . . . , accessed November 3, 2012, http:// www.youramazingbrain.org/brainchanges/stressbrain.htm.

31. "Exercise and Stress: Get Moving to Combat Stress," Mayo Clinic Staff, Mayo Clinic, July 21, 2012, http://www.mayoclinic.com/health/exercise-and-stress/ SR00036/NSECTIONGROUP= 2.

32. Ratey, *Spark*, 261; "You Can't Have One Without the Other," http://www. choosingthehealthyway.com/physicalactivityandmentalhealth.php.

33. "Movement and Learning," Bonnie's Fitware, accessed November 3, 2012, http:// www.pesoftware.com/Resources/moveLearn.html#learn.

34. Ratey, *Spark*, 32, 12.

35. "Movement," Mind, Brain, Health & Education, accessed November 3, 2012, http://www.mbhe.org/movement.

36. Ibid.

37. Ratey, *Spark*, 35.

38. "Activity Energy Expenditure and Incident Cognitive Impairment in Older Adults," Laura E. Middleton, PhD; Todd M. Manini, PhD; Eleanor M. Simonsick, PhD; Tamara B. Harris, MD, MS; Deborah E. Barnes, PhD; Frances Tylavsky, DrPH; Jennifer S. Brach, PhD, PT; James E. Everhart, MD, MPH; Kristine Yaffe, MD, The JAMA Network, July 19, 2011, http://archinte.jamanetwork.com/article.aspx?volu me=171&issue=14&page=1251.

39. "Being Active All Day Keeps the Brain Healthy," Wendy Bumgardner, About.com, August 16, 2011, http://walking.about.com/b/2011/08/16/being-more-active-all- day-keeps-brain-healthy.htm.

40. "Stand and Deliver: The Benefits of Standing at Your Desk," Reader's Digest Editors, *Reader's Digest*, accessed November 3, 2012, http://www.rd.com/health/stand-and-deliver-the-benefits-of-standing-at-your-desk/.

41. "The Reasons Why Prolonged Sitting Could Kill You and How to Avoid the Health Dangers of Sitting Too Much," February 1, 2010, http://voices.yahoo.com/the-reasons-why-prolonged-sitting-could-kill-and-5390327.html?cat=5; "Dangers of Sitting," Brooke Donald, Trib.com, July 27, 2010, http://trib.com/lifestyles/health-med-fit/health/article_16f824f1-793c-5d67-bc68-266cf469629a.html; "The Dangers of Prolonged Sitting," Chris Jones, Chris Jones Osteo, February 3, 2010, http://www.chrisjonesosteo.com.au/?p=446.

42. "Sitting for Hours Can Shave Years Off Life," William Hudson, CNN, June 24, 2011, http://edition.cnn.com/2011/HEALTH/06/24/sitting.shorten.life/index.html.

43. "The Dangers of Sitting at Work – and Standing," Bryan Walsh, Time Health & Family, April 13, 2011, http://healthland.time.com/2011/04/13/the-dangers-of-sitting-at-work%e2%80%94and-standing/.

44. "Dangers of Prolonged Sitting," Jones, http://www.chrisjonesosteo.com.au/?p=446.

45. "Extra Hour of TV a Day Can Kill," The Australian News, January 12, 2010, http://www.theaustralian.com.au/news/breaking-news/extra-hour-of-tv-a-day-can-kill-study/story-fn3dxity-1225818283014.

46. Joan Vernikos, PhD, *Sitting Kills, Moving Heals* (Fresno, CA: Quill Driver Books, 2011), 52; "Sitting for Hours," William Hudson, http://edition.cnn.com/2011/HEALTH/06/24/sitting.shorten.life/index.html.

47. "Dangers of Prolonged Sitting," Jones, http://www.chrisjonesosteo.com.au/?p=446; "Dangers of Sitting," Walsh, http://healthland.time.com/2011/04/13/the-dangers-of-sitting-at-work%e2%80%94and-standing/; "The Most Dangerous Thing You'll Do All Day," Bill Phillips, Yahoo!Health, March 30, 2011, http://health.yahoo.net/experts/menshealth/most-dangerous-thing-youll-do-all-day; "New Research Shows Surprising Dangers of Sitting!," Dr. Clay, DrClay.com, January 22, 2010, http://www.drclay.com/2010/01/new-research-shows-surprising-dangers-of-sitting/.

48. Tedd Mitchell, MD, Tim Church, MD, PhD, Martin Zucker, *Move Yourself* (Hoboken, NJ: John Wiley & Sons, Inc., 2008), 22.

49. R. Mike Mullanne, *Liftoff:An Astronaut's Dream* (Parsippany, NJ: Silver Burdett Press, 1995), 31–33.

50. Vernikos, *Sitting Kills, Moving Heals*, 19.

51. Vernikos, *Sitting Kills, Moving Heals*, 19–20.

52. "The Health Benefits of Working on Your Feet," Douglas Brown, Denver Post.com, September 5, 2011, http://www.denverpost.com/fitness/ci_18821804?source=rss.

53. "Are Standing Desks Healthier Than Sitting?" Lloyd Alter, Treehugger, February 25, 2010, http://www.treehugger.com/eco-friendly-furniture/are-standing-desks-healthier-than-sitting.html.

54. "Health Benefits," Brown, http://www.denverpost.com/fitness/ci_18821804?source=rss.

55. "Standing Desks," Alter, http://www.treehugger.com/eco-friendly-furniture/are-standing-desks-healthier-than-sitting.html.

56. "How Many Atoms Are in the Human Head?" Paul Brindza, Jefferson Lab, accessed November 3, 2012, http://education.jlab.org/qa/mathatom_03.html; Vernikos, *Sitting Kills, Moving Heals*, 61, 65.

57. Vernikos, *Sitting Kills, Moving Heals*, 36.

58. Ibid., 116.

59. Kipfer, *4,000 Questions* (New York, NY: Random House Reference, 2004), 15.

60. Dr. Todd M. Berntson, *Deskercise!* (Apple Valley, MN: Center Path Media, Inc., 2005), 128.

61. "Six Famous Siblings," Stacy, Neatorama Exclusives, Dec 2, 2008, http://www.neatorama.com/2008/12/02/six-famous-siblings/.

62. Michael McKinley, Valerie Dean O'Loughlin, *Human Anatomy* (New York, NY: McGraw-Hill, 2008), 724; "Lymphatic System," New World Encyclopedia, last modified April 3, 2008, http://www.newworldencyclopedia.org/entry/Lymphatic_system.

63. "How Blood Works," Carl Bianco, MD, Howstuffworks.com, accessed November 3, 2012, http://science.howstuffworks.com/environmental/life/human-biology/blood.htm.

64. "Lymphatic System," *New World Encyclopedia*.

65. Ibid.

66. "How Your Immune System Works," Marshall Brain, How Stuff Works, accessed November 3, 2012, http://science.howstuffworks.com/environmental/life/human-biology/immune-system.htm.

67. Ibid.

68. Ibid.

69. Ibid.

70. Michael McKinley, Valerie Dean O'Loughlin, *Human Anatomy* (New York, NY: McGraw-Hill, 2008), 727.

71. "Phagocytosis," *Encyclopedia Britannica*, accessed November 3, 2012, http://www.britannica.com/EBchecked/topic/454919/phagocytosis.

72. "T-cell-mediated Cytotoxicity," NCBI, accessed November 3, 2012, http://www.ncbi.nlm.nih.gov/books/NBK27101/.

73. Ibid.; "Natural Killer Cell Activity," Jacquelyn Jeanty, eHowMom, accessed November 3, 2012, http://www.ehow.com/about_6136390_natural-killer-cell-activity.html.

74. McKinley and O'Loughlin, *Human Anatomy*, 728.

75. "The Lymphatic System – One of the Body's Largest Organs," Karen Davis, Ezine Articles, accessed November 3, 2012, http://ezinearticles.com/?The-Lymphatic-System---One-of-the-Bodys-Largest-Organs&id=6669311.

76. McKinley and O'Loughlin, Human Anatomy, 723.

77. "Lymphatic System," New World Encyclopedia, accessed November 3, 2012, http://www.newworldencyclopedia.org/entry/Lymphatic_system.

78. "Lymph Node," Wikipedia, accessed November 3, 2012, http://en.wikipedia.org/wiki/Lymph_follicle.

79. "Lymph and the Lymphatic System," Lymphedema Association of Saskatchewan, accessed November 3, 2012, http://www.sasklymph.ca/lymph_system.php.

80. "How Does the Human Body Eliminate Dead Cells?" Wisegeek, accessed November 3, 2012, http://www.wisegeek.com/how-does-the-human-body-eliminate-dead-cells.htm.

81. "Interstitial Fluid," Answers.com, accessed November 3, 2012, http://www.answers.com/topic/interstitial-fluid-2.

82. "How to Clean the Lymphatic System," Ramona French, ehow.com, accessed November 3, 2012, http://www.ehow.com/how_7871520_clean-lymphatic-system.html.

83. Ibid.

84. Ibid.

85. Kipfer, *4,000 Questions* (New York, NY: Random House Reference, 2004), 100.

86. Garry Poole, *The Complete Book of Questions* (Grand Rapids, MI: Zondervan, 2003), 105.

87. Shirley Archer, *Fitness 9 to 5* (San Francisco, CA: Chronicle Books, 2006), 44.

88. "Should You Wait an Hour After Eating Before You Go Swimming?" SixWise.com, accessed November 2, 2012, http://www.sixwise.com/newsletters/06/03/15/should-you-wait-an-hour-after-eating-before-you-go-swimming.htm.

89. Mitchell, Church, and Zucker, *Move Yourself*, 4, 6.

90. American Heart Association, *Fitting In Fitness* (New York, NY: Clarkson Potter/Publishers, 1997), 22.

91. Florida Hospital Mission Development, *Creation Health Seminar Personal Study Guide* (2009), 108.

92. Ibid., 109.

93. Sean Foy, *The 10-Minute Total Body Breakthrough* (New York, NY: Workman Publishing, 2009), 92, 102, 122, 113, 160, 199.

94. Ibid.

95. Al Sears, M.D., *P.A.C.E.* (Royal Palm Beach, FL: Wellness Research & Consulting, Inc., 2010).

96. Ralph Gower, *The New Manners and Customs of Bible Times* (Chicago, IL: Moody Bible Institute, 1987), 153–154.

97. Reader's Digest, *Jesus and His Times* (Pleasantville, NY: The Reader's Digest Association, Inc., 1987), 111–112.

98. "How Far Did Jesus Walk in His Lifetime?" Yahoo! answers, accessed November 3, 2012, http://uk.answers.yahoo.com/question/index?qid=20100120131205AAd9kTA.

99. Poole, *Complete Book of Questions*, 69, 37.

100. Barbara Templeton and Jamie Templeton, *The Complete Idiot's Guide to Stretching* (New York, NY: Penguin Group, 2007), 73.

101. Andrea L. Dunn, PhD, Bess H. Marcus, PhD, James B. Kampert, PhD, Melissa E. Garcia, MPH, Harold W. Kohl III, PhD, Steven N. Blair, PED, "Comparison of Lifestyle and Structured Interventions to Increase Physical Activity and Cardiorespiratory Fitness," A Randomized Trial, August 1, 1993, through July 31, 1997, *Journal of the American Medical Association*, http://jama.ama-assn.org/content/281/4/327.full.pdf+html.

102. Amanda Chan, "Chores Count As Working Out: Study," *Huffington Post*, June 29, 2011, http://www.huffingtonpost.com/2011/06/29/chores-everyday.fitness_n_887000.html#s300652&title=Walking_Up_Stairs; "Household Chores: The New Workout Regime," Kathleen McCracken, Examiner.com, August 7, 2010, http://www.examiner.com/article/household-chores-the-new-workout-regime.

103. Florida Hospital Mission Development, *Creation Health Seminar Personal Study Guide* (2009), 111.

104. "Fitness Around the Clock," Llee Sivitz, Cincinnati.com, August 13, 2001, http://enquirer.com/editions/2001/08/13/tem_fitness_around_clock.html.

105. "5 Everyday Activities That Can Burn Calories (Almost) Like a Workout," Grace Lazenby, Livestrong.com, April 26, 2011, http://www.livestrong.com/article/5906-everyday-activities-that-can-burn/.

106. "Changing Regular Activities Into Exercise for Weight Loss," WeSlim.com, accessed November 3, 2012, http://www.weslim.com/regularexercise.html.

107. "How to Get Fit Through Daily Activity," Donna McKinney, *Suite101*, December 30, 2009, http://donna-mckinney.suite101.com/how-to-get-fit-through-daily-activity-a184050.

108. "Turning Life's Daily Activities into Fun Exercise," Nexercise, Dec 1, 2011, http://www.nexercise.com/2011/12/turning-life%e2%80%99s-daily-activities-into-fun-exercise/.

109. Ibid.

110. "Hobbies and Everyday Chores Can Become Exercise Sessions," Women's Healthcare Issues, June 6, 2011, http://womenshealthcareissues.com/hobbies_everyday_chores_exerci.html.

111. American Heart Association, *Fitting in Fitness* (New York, NY: Clarkson Potter/Publishers, 1997), 113.

112. Ibid., 24.

113. Ibid., 65.

114. "Sitting Slows Metabolism - How to Not Sit Still?" Wendy Bumgardner, About.com, last updated March 8, 2012, http://walking.about.com/od/goodmedicine/a/sitting092007.htm.

115. American Heart Association, *Fitting in Fitness*, 113.

116. Ibid., 115.

117. "5 Everyday Activities," Lazenby, http://www.livestrong.com/article/5906-everyday-activities-that-can-burn/.

118. American Heart Association, *Fitting in Fitness*, 22–23.

119. "Fitness Around the Clock," Sivitz, http://enquirer.com/editions/2001/08/13/tem_fitness_around_clock.html.

120. American Heart Association, *Fitting in Fitness*, 21.

121. Charlene Torkelson, *Get Fit While You Sit* (Alameda, CA: Hunter House Inc. Publishers, 1999), 96.

122. American Heart Association, *Fitting In Fitness* (New York, NY: Clarkson Potter/Publishers, 1997), 147.

123. Shirley Archer, *Fitness 9 to 5* (San Francisco, CA: Chronicle Books, 2006), 116–117.

124. Berntson, *Deskercise*, 64.

125. Ibid., 70.

126. Torkelson, *Get Fit While You Sit,* 23.

127. Ibid., 76–77.

128. Mitchell, Church, Zucker, *Move Yourself*, 101; "How Much Cardio Exercise Does it Take to Really Get Fit?" Russell Dean Cantwell, Ezine articles, November 3, 2012, http://ezinearticles.com/?How-Much-Cardio-Exercise-Does-it-Take-to-Really-Get-Fit?&id=2238753.

129. Poole, *The Complete Book of Questions*, 90.

130. Jerry D. Jones, *201 Great Questions* (Colorado Springs, CO: NavPress, 1988), 15.

131. Bob Anderson, *Stretching* (Bolinas, CA: Shelter Publications, Inc., 2010), 55.

132. Jim, "The White Mountains: A Beautiful Place to Die," *Free New Hampshire Blog*, August 19, 2008, http://www.freenewhampshireblog.com/index.php/2008/08/19/the-white-mountains-a-beautiful-place-to-die/.

133. Mitchell, Church, and Zucker, *Move Yourself*, 14.

134. "Coping With Acne: Your Care Plan," Peter Jaret, WebMD, accessed November 3, 2012, http://www.webmd.com/skin-problems-and-treatments/acne/acne-care-11/exercise.

135. "Better Sleep, Prettier Skin and 8 Other Unexpected Side Benefits of Working Out," Schocker, *Huffington Post*, March 23, 2012, http://www.huffingtonpost.com/2012/3/23/exercise-hcalth_n_1374389.html?ref=health-fitness#s806430&title=Improved_Sexual_Function.

136. Mitchell, Church, and Zucker, *Move Yourself*, 14.

137. "Better Sleep, Prettier Skin," Schocker, http://www.huffingtonpost.com/2012/3/23/exercise-health_n_1374389.html?ref=health-fitness#s806430&title=Improved_Sexual_Function.

138. "Sudden Impacts," Martin Padgett, Jr., www.DoctorPaddock.com, accessed November 3, 2012, http://home.comcast.net/~bradpa/Exercise.htm.

139. "Immediate Effects of Exercise on the Body," Brian Connolly, Livestrong.com, June 14, 2011, http://www.livestrong.com/article/447358-immediate-effects-of-exercise-on-the-body/.

140. "Better Sleep, Prettier Skin," Schocker, http://www.huffingtonpost.com/2012/3/23/exercise-health_n_1374389.html?ref=health-fitness#s806430&title=Improved_Sexual_Function.

141. Running & FitNews, "Exercise for Mood, With Immediate Results," May 14, 2012, http://findarticles.com/p/articles/mi_m0NHF/is_1_24/ai_n16676513/.

142. Mitchell, Church, and Zucker, *Move Yourself*, 82.

143. Monica Reed, M.D., *The Creation Health Breakthrough* (New York, NY: Center Street, 2007), 109.

144. "Immediate Effects," Connolly, http://www.livestrong.com/article/447358-immediate-effects-of-exercise-on-the-body/.

145. "6 Health Benefits of Exercise," Jennifer R. Scott, About.com, July 26, 2010, http://weightloss.about.com/od/exercise/a/bl_exerben.htm.

146. Mitchell, Church, and Zucker, *Move Yourself*, 14.

147. Mitchell, Church, and Zucker, *Move Yourself*, 76.

148. Sears, *P.A.C.E.*, 10.

149. "The Immediate Benefits of Exercise," Morgan Craig-Broadwith, Live It Active, March 26, 2011, http://liveitactive.wordpress.com/2011/03/26/the-immediate-benefits-of-exercise/; Mitchell, Church, and Zucker, Move Yourself, 83–84.

150. "Benefits of Exercise," www.DoctorPaddock.com, http://home.comcast.net/~bradpa/Exercise.htm.

151. Sears, *P.A.C.E.*, 16–17, 43.

152. "Why You Need to Exercise," Jennifer R. Scott, About.com, December 22, 2008, http://weightloss.about.com/od/exercis1/a/aa080807a.htm.

153. Mitchell, Church, and Zucker, *Move Yourself*, 90.

154. Mitchell, Church, and Zucker, *Move Yourself*, 143.

155. "Immediate Benefits," Craig-Broadwith, http://liveitactive.wordpress.com/2011/03/26/the-immediate-benefits-of-exercise/.

156. "10 Reasons to Encourage Fitness in the Workplace," Bob Doyle, SelfGrowth.com, http://www.selfgrowth.com/articles/doyle4.html.

157. Mitchell, Church, and Zucker, *Move Yourself*, 36.

158. Bob Anderson, *Stretching* (Bolinas, CA: Shelter Publications, Inc., 2010), 46.

159. "Glass Bowl Bought for £1 Valued at £25,000 by *Antiques Roadshow* Experts," STV Glasgow, December 22, 2008, http://local.stv.tv/glasgow/66571-glass-bowl-bought-for-pound1-valued-at-pound25000-by-antiques-roadshow-experts/.

160. Vernikos, *Sitting Kills, Moving Heals*, vii.

LEAD YOUR COMMUNITY
TO HEALTHY
LIVING

INCLUDES ONLINE TRAINING

Seminar Leader Kit
Everything a leader needs to conduct this seminar successfully, including key questions to facilitate group discussion and PowerPoint presentations for each of the eight principles.

Participant Guide
A study guide with essential information from each of the eight lessons along with outlines, self assessments, and questions for people to fill-in as they follow along.

Small Group Kit
It's easy to lead a small group using the CREATION Health videos, the Small Group Leaders Guide and the Small Group Discussion Guide.

CREATION Kids
CREATION Health Kids can make a big difference in homes, schools and congregations. Lead kids in your community to healthier, happier living.

Life Guide Series
These guides include questions designed to help individuals or small groups study the depths of every principle and learn strategies for integrating them into everyday life.

GUIDES AND ASSESSMENTS

Pregnancy Guides
Expert advice on how to be CREATION Healthy while expecting.

Senior Guide
Share the CREATION Health principles with seniors and help them be healthier and happier as they live life to the fullest.

Self-Assessment
This instrument raises awareness about how CREATION Healthy a person is in each of the eight major areas of wellness.

Pocket Guide
A tool for keeping people committed to living all of the CREATION Health principles daily.

Tote Bag
A convenient way for bringing CREATION Health materials to and from class.

Tumbler
Practice good Nutrition and keep yourself hydrated with a CREATION Health tumbler in an assortment of fun colors.

MARKETING MATERIALS

Postcards, Posters, Stationary, and more
You can effectively advertise and generate community excitement about your CREATION Health seminar with a wide range of available marketing materials such as enticing postcards, flyers, posters, and more.

Bible Stories
God is interested in our physical, mental and spiritual well being. Throughout the Bible you can discover the eight principles for full life.

CREATION HEALTH BOOKS

CREATION Health Discovery
Written by Des Cummings, Jr., PhD and Monica Reed, MD, this wonderful companion resource introduces people to the CREATION Health philosophy and lifestyle.

CREATION Health Devotional
In this devotional you will discover stories about experiencing God's grace in the tough times, God's delight in triumphant times, and God's presence in peaceful times.

English: Hardcover
Spanish: Softcover

CREATION Health Discovery (Softcover)

CREATION Health Discovery takes the 8 essential principles of CREATION Health and melds them together to form the blueprint for the health we yearn for and the life we are intended to live.

CREATION Health Breakthrough (Hardcover)

Blending science and lifestyle recommendations, Monica Reed, MD, prescribes eight essentials that will help reverse harmful health habits and prevent disease. Discover how intentional choices, rest, environment, activity, trust, relationships, outlook, and nutrition can put a person on the road to wellness. Features a three-day total body rejuvenation therapy and four-phase life transformation plan.

CREATION Health Devotional (English: Hardcover / Spanish: Softcover)

Stories change lives. Stories can inspire health and healing. In this devotional you will discover stories about experiencing God's grace in the tough times, God's delight in triumphant times, and God's presence in peaceful times. Based on the eight timeless principles of wellness: Choice, Rest, Environment, Activity, Trust, Interpersonal relationships, Outlook, Nutrition.

CREATION Health Devotional for Women (English)

Written for women by women, the *CREATION Health Devotional for Women* is based on the principles of whole-person wellness represented in CREATION Health. Spirits will be lifted and lives rejuvenated by the message of each unique chapter. This book is ideal for women's prayer groups, to give as a gift, or just to buy for your own edification and encouragement.

8 Secrets of a Healthy 100 (Softcover)

Can you imagine living to a Healthy 100 years of age? Dr. Des Cummings Jr., explores the principles practiced by the All-stars of Longevity to live longer and more abundantly. Take a journey through the 8 Secrets and you will be inspired to imagine living to a Healthy 100.

Forgive To Live (English: Hardcover / Spanish: Softcover)

In *Forgive to Live* Dr. Tibbits presents the scientifically proven steps for forgiveness – taken from the first clinical study of its kind conducted by Stanford University and Florida Hospital.

Forgive To Live Workbook (Softcover)

This interactive guide will show you how to forgive – insight by insight, step by step – in a workable plan that can effectively reduce your anger, improve your health, and put you in charge of your life again, no matter how deep your hurts.

Forgive To Live Devotional (Hardcover)

In his powerful new devotional Dr. Dick Tibbits reveals the secret to forgiveness. This compassionate devotional is a stirring look at the true meaning of forgiveness. Each of the 56 spiritual insights includes motivational Scripture, an inspirational prayer, and two thought-provoking questions. The insights are designed to encourage your journey as you begin to *Forgive to Live*.

Forgive To Live God's Way (Softcover)

Forgiveness is so important that our very lives depend on it. Churches teach us that we should forgive, but how do you actually learn to forgive? In this spiritual workbook noted author, psychologist, and ordained minister Dr. Dick Tibbits takes you step-by-step through an eight-week forgiveness format that is easy to understand and follow.

Forgive To Live Leader's Guide

Perfect for your community, church, small group or other settings.
The Forgive to Live Leader's Guide Includes:

- 8 Weeks of pre-designed PowerPoint™ presentations.
- Professionally designed customizable marketing materials and group handouts on CD-Rom.
- Training directly from author of Forgive to Live Dr. Dick Tibbits across 6 audio CDs.
- Media coverage DVD.
- CD-Rom containing all files in digital format for easy home or professional printing.
- A copy of the first study of its kind conducted by Stanford University and Florida Hospital showing a link between decreased blood pressure and forgiveness.

52 Ways to Feel Great Today (Softcover)

Wouldn't you love to feel great today? Changing your outlook and injecting energy into your day often begins with small steps. In *52 Ways to Feel Great Today*, you'll discover an abundance of simple, inexpensive, fun things you can do to make a big difference in how you feel today and every day. Tight on time? No problem. Each chapter is written as a short, easy-to-implement idea. Every idea is supported by at least one true story showing how helpful implementing the idea has proven to someone a lot like you. The stories are also included to encourage you to be as inventive, imaginative, playful, creative, or adventuresome as you can.

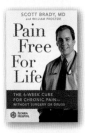

Pain Free For Life (Hardcover)

In *Pain Free For Life*, Scott C. Brady, MD, – founder of Florida Hospital's Brady Institute for Health – shares for the first time with the general public his dramatically successful solution for chronic back pain, Fibromyalgia, chronic headaches, Irritable bowel syndrome and other "impossible to cure" pains. Dr. Brady leads pain-racked readers to a pain-free life using powerful mind-body-spirit strategies used at the Brady Institute – where more than 80 percent of his chronic-pain patients have achieved 80-100 percent pain relief within weeks.

If Today Is All I Have (Softcover)

At its heart, Linda's captivating account chronicles the struggle to reconcile her three dreams of experiencing life as a "normal woman" with the tough realities of her medical condition. Her journey is punctuated with insights that are at times humorous, painful, provocative, and life-affirming.

SuperSized Kids (Hardcover)

In *SuperSized Kids*, Walt Larimore, MD, and Sherri Flynt, MPH, RD, LD, show how the mushrooming childhood obesity epidemic is destroying children's lives, draining family resources, and pushing America dangerously close to a total healthcare collapse – while also explaining, step by step, how parents can work to avert the coming crisis by taking control of the weight challenges facing every member of their family.

SuperFit Family Challenge – Leader's Guide

Perfect for your community, church, small group or other settings.
The SuperFit Family Challenge Leader's Guide Includes:
- 8 Weeks of pre-designed PowerPoint™ presentations.
- Professionally designed marketing materials and group handouts from direct mailers to reading guides.
- Training directly from Author Sherri Flynt, MPH, RD, LD, across 6 audio CDs.
- Media coverage and FAQ on DVD.

NOTES:

IMAGINE...

A body that is healthy and strong,
A spirit that is vibrant and refreshed,
A life that glorifies God,
Imagine living to a **Healthy 100**.